Fourth Witness

Kit Widdows

WRITERSWORLD

Published by WRITERSWORLD

Copyright © Kit Widdows 2004

Cover design by Steve Foote2004 ©

The moral right of the author has been asserted

ISBN 1-904181-33-3

WRITERSWORLD
9 Manor Close
Enstone
Oxfordshire,
OX7 4LU,
England

www.writersworld.co.uk

For Gillian

Prologue

Love began it.
Love is how God tells it.
Love is God.
Love lights a living lantern in the dark
        and its gentle strength wins over every shadow.

Love is not a Thing.
So those who say 'to know' means 'know about' cannot
'know' Love.
Love has no atoms and no molecules;
Love rates low in an 'Enlightened' age.

Love became human; an animal, and God.
And all who understand this themselves become all three.

Love came camping with us;
By day we climbed the hills,
        discovering hidden lakes and unexpected views;
By night we drank and talked,
        discovering hidden views and unexpected depths.

We have shared all this
        from the First Sign to the Last Supper:
Love's lantern burns in us
        and we in turn must light a lamp
Enlightening a world which,
        glitter-blind, does not know Love.

Chapter 1

Jesus was fidgeting. This was uncomfortable, as I was leaning against him on the couch. It was not surprising, after the stress of the last few days, never knowing whether we would suddenly be engulfed in a hail of stones or arrested by the police. But it was unusual. I still felt a sense of strong self-assurance from him, a curious and uncomfortable peace, but at the same time he was tense and edgy.

Then, with one of his swift and decisive movements, and with less than half an apology to me as I had to save myself from falling, he was on his feet and taking off his cloak.

The conversations round the tables stopped dead. Apart, that is, from Peter, who, half-turned on his elbow and with his back to the top couch, was saying to Martha, '...thunder or no thunder...' His half-phrase hung in the sudden silence as he twisted himself round to follow Jesus with his eyes. Just as we all did.

Jesus had gone over to the basin and towel left on the floor in the corner. Of course, no one had washed either his feet or anyone else's. He'd ask one of the younger ones to do it. I relaxed back slightly, just brushing Judas's feet on the couch, and half-smiling at him, but he was miles away. These days he seemed almost unreachable.

Jesus approached Philip. Open and straightforward, Philip wouldn't make any difficulties about doing a servant's work. I felt the tension drain out of the moment. And then Jesus was on his knees at Philip's feet, edging the table aside slightly with his left shoulder as he slid a sandal onto the floor and began pouring handfuls of water over the ankles and letting it run back into the basin. Philip tried to jerk back, but Jesus had

3

him in a firm grip, and with a rapid and economical twitch, had the towel around the now-washed foot and was rubbing it dry. A glance at Philip dared him to move or even open his mouth in protest and Jesus pulled his other foot off the couch and repeated the process. Philip had turned white with shock and there was even a tic of anger in his cheek and a tightening of his lips as Jesus smiled full in his face, and laid a damp and careless finger on his disciple's mouth.

The table creaked and slid even further out of line as Jesus shouldered his way to Nathaniel who was reclining in the centre of the couch next to Philip. Nathaniel had both feet up on the couch and twisted under him as he guessed Jesus' intention, and he was about to offer, demand even, that he take over the task, as indeed several of us were. Mary had risen from her chair, and in her mind, as in ours, was the picture of her own washing of Jesus' feet a few days ago. The words were forming on her lips. Nathaniel, Mary, myself, all of us were halted with our protests still-born as Jesus swept us with a look. Dominating and commanding, from his servant's crouch on the floor squeezed between the table and Nathaniel's knees, his eyes flashed his demand for obedience and compliance. Mary sank back onto her chair, something that was almost a growl subsided in Peter's throat, and reluctantly Nathaniel unwound his legs so that Jesus could wash his feet.

Andrew was lying against Nathaniel, and his feet were the most accessible on that couch, being stuck out over the end. In any case, sunny, generous Andrew would let Jesus do anything, however unusual or improper. As I thought of that, I suddenly realised that for most of us the offence lay not in Jesus doing this thing because he was Jesus, but rather that he had offended our notions of propriety. It was not so much that one of us should have done it anyway (although there was more than a twinge of guilt attached to that thought), but that Jesus had gone the wrong way about putting matters right. Why hadn't he *said* something, instead of taking it on

4

himself? I certainly didn't want him to wash my feet, and I was already wondering about the ready phrase that might persuade him to let us swap roles. He was always telling me I had a silver tongue. Surely I was close enough and senior enough to get away with it. Something of a word-play, maybe a pun or a paradox, Jesus loved them. Perhaps something about a chance to serve being liberating - no, too political, especially this week - maybe that serving him is perfect freedom. Yes. That would do.

Jesus had finished the three lying on the lower couch, and I expected him to come to Judas and myself on the top couch next, before making his way round to Thomas, Peter and James on the right-hand couch. But he didn't. He got up from Andrew and moved into the middle, where some of the women were seated in chairs. Again, the look. Again silence commanded and protest stifled, as he dropped down at the feet of Mary. He was going to wash a woman's feet too! And there was I thinking about impropriety while he was still with the men! Judas went totally rigid. I suddenly felt his coiled anger and, well - yes - *hatred*. No other word for it. Intuitively I saw it though his eyes. He was remembering the dinner given four days ago at Bethany where Mary had anointed and washed Jesus' feet, and Jesus had reprimanded Judas for trying to intervene. That had been shocking enough, and now here was Jesus returning the compliment to a woman and more-or-less in public. Judas was taking this very, very personally. He was seeing it as a total condemnation of his attitude to Mary and her behaviour last Sunday. I felt some compassion for him. Jesus was not renowned for sympathy for those with whom he disagreed, but he had moved at this point from the improper to the blatantly shocking. At least it would now come to an end. He had made his point.

I could see that Martha felt the same. She was sitting next to her sister, who was smiling unaffectedly at Jesus as he finished wiping her feet and twinkled up at her. I could almost feel the unspoken message - 'Now if *I* had *your* hair, we could really shock them...'

But this was to be an evening of surprise upon surprise. Jesus did not stand up, having made his point, but did a neat double shuffle on his knees, and was now at Martha's feet. Her slipper was in his hand and laid aside, and the handfuls of (now not entirely clean) water were sluicing over her left foot. I waited for the explosion. *No-one* did this to Martha. She was sitting bolt upright, rigid, and two red spots burnt high on cheeks that had gone almost sallow. She was the only one among us who had actually said out loud that Jesus was our expected Messiah (or Christ), and here he was at her feet. No Messiah would stoop to this. Was he denying her faith and insight? And then suddenly she relaxed and stretched out her right foot. My eyes had been fixed on her, and I now noticed that Jesus' were too. Some message had passed, and Martha, yes, Martha of all of us, was content to let it happen. Well, not content precisely, she was still very uncomfortable about it, but assenting. What had passed between them? Had Jesus half glanced at Lazarus, down at one of the other tables set out below the couches? It seemed that whatever had passed between Jesus and Martha was to do with that moment of truth close by the tomb, and while Martha continued to disapprove of Jesus' action, yet she sensed it was part of the same life that he had restored to Lazarus and offered to her.

Jesus passed to the other Mary, a Northerner like myself (and many of us), and less caught up in the excessive etiquette of the Judæan south. She had no objections to having her feet washed by Jesus, and had her slippers off ready for the water. She also didn't mind (as Martha surely had) it's dusty and discoloured nature, which it had rapidly acquired from Philip, Nathaniel and Andrew. I realised that for Mary it was the gesture itself that mattered, and indeed that was the case in general for the women, and I was becoming uncomfortably aware that no flippancy or neat phrase on my part would change Jesus' mind. This was about far more than who should have washed our feet and far, far more than being clean and comfortable for dinner. I saw that I would have to go through with this.

The other women done, Jesus came to the top table. Judas was first, the hatred still blazing in his eyes. He was convinced that this was all done to humiliate him. And in that curious way of his, he wanted to draw and hug his hurt to himself. He swung his feet down off the couch almost eagerly, as if he couldn't wait for the insult to be complete. I looked down at Jesus' face, only inches away from mine now, and saw his expression as he gazed up at Judas. There was trouble in his eyes, trouble reflecting a troubled soul that was rare in Jesus, so often confident against all odds and all expectation. There was love too, absorbing and refracting Judas' hate and hurt, but it seemed as if Jesus was infinitely the more hurt of the two.

He seemed to be saying 'Judas, this is not against you, it is *for* you', as if the most important thing in the world was that, when the hard times would come, Judas should remember that his feet were washed clean, and by whom.

I dared not turn my face up to look at Judas, but I felt him go cold and closed. He would not, could not, accept the offer, the challenge implied by Jesus' face. I felt the tension rippling through his body and the trembling where we touched on the couch, but it was all of denial. It was as if, on our couch, the dark had come out.

Jesus gave a little shrug of his body, as if to shake loose of the moment, and he was at my feet now. No ready phrase came to my lips, but his were quirking as if he well knew what I had planned to say and do. As ever, he was ahead of me, and I was still stunned by the dark moment the three of us had shared, here at the head of the tables, but all his attention was on me now.

I saw that he was aware that I had been thinking of

propriety and prestige, and felt his thought, 'Forget yourself, Beloved, my love is more than status.'

Ashamed, I thought of leaving the couch and taking a seat at the other end of the room, and realised that Jesus' smile had now broadened into a full-hearted grin that said, 'Typical, that's just as self-centred! Why not just be where you are? Go with the flow!'

He paused for a moment, my right foot still in his hand, and I remember noticing inconsequentially that the towel was now too wet to be of any use, as he gazed up at me in trust and humour. 'If *you* don't understand, Beloved, what must the others be thinking?'

As ever, his humour, even at its most ironical, called up a little bubble of mirth inside me, and I found myself grinning openly in response. For a second the moment held, just Jesus and I were alone together in the crowded room, and my heart full of his infuriating, indefinable challenge that was always so close and always dancing just beyond my reach. Oh, Jesus!

Then he was gone. He had felt my silly thought about the towel, for he picked up another as he went to wash the feet of those at the other tables. He had clearly decided to leave the right-hand couch for the last. Given that Thomas, Peter and James were sharing that one, I could imagine why. If there was going to be trouble, Martha being safely negotiated, it would be on that couch. For myself, I was still locked in that moment with Jesus, treasuring his grin, and realising again how he continually teased and challenged me. I was sure Martha was right, that he was the Messiah, but if this were true, I needed to change my whole way of thinking about what that implied. Jesus was a Northerner, from Nazareth, and taught and thought little of King David. He had in my hearing resisted kingly claims and avoided any attempt to gain political status or support.

I had personal experience of Essene teaching, and had spent time with the Baptist and knew what was expected of the Messiah. Jesus went to some lengths to contradict these expectations. On the other hand, he had told a Samaritan woman that he was the Christ, and, while Samaritan expectations are rather different from ours, still, it seemed clear enough at the time.

Somehow he was in another league. Yes, another league beyond our deepest and highest hopes. He seemed to take the messianic ideal merely as first base for something far wilder and more godly, and I felt that I half glimpsed it and half fell trailing behind as he made more and more dangerous and impossible claims upon my belief and commitment. What I did understand was that it was something that I could never, never walk away from. God was doing something unprecedented, and it was focused on Jesus.

And apart from all that, I loved him, and he loved me. The bond was deep and affectionate and bound us together at a level quite different from the theology and the controversy and the adrenaline flow of being with him in public and private.

Jesus had now nearly finished. He was at the feet of Joseph by the door. Joseph had come late and would leave early. He was an aristocrat, and afraid of losing his position and influence if it were ever discovered that he kept company with Jesus. But for all that he was a disciple. Jesus had worked his magic on him too, and Joseph couldn't let go any more than I could. Was he a coward, or merely prudent? How real is the difference? In any case, it might well be that we would need friends in high places before all this was over. Jesus was glancing up at Joseph as he dried his second foot. I well understood by now that there would be an exchange going on as significant for Joseph as it had been for me and for each of us.

Finally he returned to Peter's couch and knelt to wash James' feet. No trouble there. James seemed curiously limp, as if watching and waiting had taken all the bluster from him. His face seemed to say that he would be glad when it was all over and the charade at an end. I could see Jesus was looking up at him, and he seemed to brace himself slightly, and the beginnings of a rueful smile lit his eyes as he tucked his feet back over the bottom end of the couch.

Thomas too, unusually, maintained his silence. I assumed that his view was along the lines of 'You can do what you like in private, Jesus, but do please keep your head down a bit in public, and for Heaven's sake, don't let this story get out in the wrong places - washing women's feet...'

I could imagine Jesus' reply; '"For Heaven's sake," Thomas? Wrong thinking; right idea...'

Thomas liked to believe that he was more realistic than the rest of us, that he took 'the long view' and that what Jesus had stirred up could only end in tears. He *did* believe this, but not as much as he liked to pretend, especially to himself. There was a hidden optimist in Thomas that occasionally peeped out, to his embarrassment, and Jesus loved to tease it out of him. I could guess that this was what was happening between them now.

Jesus had left Peter to the last, and Peter had clearly been thinking it through. He had his feet tucked so far behind him that he was almost kneeling in the centre of the couch, and leaning forward to tower over Jesus. His face was brick red and when he spoke, the first of us to break that long silence that had been so full of communication, it was with a dangerously calm and level voice.

'My feet too? Do you propose to do this to me?' It was clear that he was ready to argue, and had a dozen reasons ready why Jesus should not wash his feet. Or if not a dozen reasons, one or two that he was prepared to repeat a dozen times.

'Simon, you don't understand. Let me finish with your feet now, and I will explain.'

10

Peter should have noticed the 'Simon', which always meant he was missing the point. But he had his line ready; 'Never, Lord, not me. Not for all eternity.'

Jesus sat back on his haunches, and was almost chuckling. Trust Peter to pick the wrong thing to say. Jesus dropped the towel and reaching up laid a hand on Peter's forearm.

'But that's the point, Peter.' (He was 'Peter' again.) 'It *is* for eternity. If you don't let me do this, you're not a part of it. More to the point, not a part of me and mine.

Even on his dignity, Peter could never resist Jesus' gentle mockery coupled with that loving tone of entreaty. Peter's dignity was usually slightly comical, but he knew when to let it go, and he did so now, rather like a father indulging a favourite daughter as he twisted round to give Jesus his feet. But he still wasn't finished. Maybe he'd known he would lose this one, and he had more to say.

Putting his feet full in the basin, and leaning right over it, he said, 'Well, if that's the way of it, here are my hands and head, wash them too!'

Peter could dwarf Jesus when he chose, and this was one of those moments, with him leaning over the basin from the couch, and Jesus squatting in front of him. Both of them were laughing full into each other's eyes. Most of the rest of us were grinning in sympathy. Peter hadn't meant to do it, but somehow the whole foot-washing episode seemed to become more fitting, more proportionate.

Jesus laid his hand affectionately around Peter's neck, and pointedly tracing his finger along the tide-mark that declared Peter had not been swimming for some time, said, 'Regular bathers don't need the full treatment - you are clean enough for me.' And with that he gave Peter a shove back onto the couch, and deftly grabbed and washed first one foot and then the other.

As he did this, however, the smile faded, and sensing his change of mood we fell silent again, awaiting his words.

'Oh yes, you are clean enough for me, but not all of you are!'

Fourth Witness

The unease and distress that had been so much part of the earlier moments rushed back in on us. I started to turn to look at Judas, next to me on the couch, but thought better of it. In utter silence Jesus deposited the bowl and towel in a corner and returned to the couch. He paused to resume his cloak, still lying on the floor behind our couch, and I felt rather than saw him slide back into his place between Judas and myself.

In the total suspense and stillness he slowly looked round at us all.

He spoke.

'Have you any idea what it is that I have just done for you?'

Chapter 2

You have been introduced into the middle of things, and names will be running round your head. Before I tell you how Jesus explained why he washed our feet - another of his famous signs - I should explain a little of who we are and how we came to be there. Perhaps the best way to help you to understand this is to tell you how it started for some of us.

I have said I am a Northerner, and I am proud of it, but in fact I had been brought up in Jerusalem as much as Galilee, and my family has houses in both places. From as early as I can remember, I have been fascinated by religion and by religious behaviour, and as a young man I spent quite a bit of time with the Essenes in Jerusalem.

These are a group, or rather a group of groups, who take the Bible most seriously, especially when it comes to ritual, purity and the like. The ones that I encountered in Jerusalem are by no means as strict as some, but nevertheless quite an eye-opener for a lad brought up in a liberal family. These Essenes had little time for the priesthood, and for the Temple under its present administration, and that will form a part of the story later on. They expected the Messiah to come very soon, and indeed more than one Messiah, and told their own stories about what would happen at that time. Like all the ultra-religious, they felt they had a hot line to God, that they would be his favourites when the crisis came, and that everyone else would then be punished for not realising that the Essenes had been right all along. This I found both fascinating and deeply off-putting.

A few years ago, I heard that a certain John, having been a fellow-traveller of the Essenes, had struck out on his own, and was preparing people for the Messiah by baptising them at various places up and down the Jordan Valley. John the

Baptist, as he was soon labelled, quickly became all the news, at least in religious circles, and I was curious. His message touched a nerve in me, as he too seemed to have thrown off the narrow self-thinking of the Essenes, but retained their belief that God was about to write a new chapter in the history of world. John thought, as I did, that this would be to do with the coming Messiah.

I was friends with Simon (whom we now call Peter) and Andrew. They were our one-time playmates on our frequent visits to Bethsaida, just north of the Sea of Galilee, and Andrew too was curious about the Baptist. We decided to take off for the winter, and stay with John. You may say that for a period we became his disciples.

It was fascinating. John had taken the best of Messianic thinking, and applied it not to a chosen few, but to whomever chose to listen. He claimed that he was simply there to act as a witness to the Messiah who was already here. Now this was confusing. There were so many different ideas about the Messiah, all fervently held by different groups and teachers, that it was very easy to lose your way in the muddle. This muddle applied as much to the religious specialists as to the rest of us, and Andrew and I happened to be present at one of their several attempts at a trial of John.

You should understand that we Jews tend to deal with legal matters (and matters of religion are the most important matters of law, of course) in the open, and in terms of discussion and debate between accusers and accused. We are not keen on the Western way with courts and advocates whose job it is to twist the truth, and we like our judgments speedy, simple and direct. We like to think that we are more interested in truth and character than in logic-chopping and bribery.

It began one afternoon when John had just left the river and was drying off on the bank at Bethany. (Not the famous

Bethany, but the one just across the river in Peræa, part of Herod's territory.) A deputation had arrived from the Temple authorities who clearly had instructions to conduct a trial of John and his claims. Their spokesman was a relative of mine, and wisely he began not with an accusation but with a question.

'As your message is concerning the Messiah, who do you claim to be?'

I say it was not an accusation, which was wise, considering John had a large following there, but there was a hidden implication, and John immediately saw through it.

'I am not the Messiah.'

'Are you Elijah?' was the next question.

This was harder, for John *was* claiming to point to the Messiah, and many scholars thought that this role would be fulfilled by the renewal of prophecy in Israel, just as Elijah had effectively been the first of the great Biblical prophets. But knowing the rules, John denied this too. Within the strict terms of the law, such a claim would lead to endless trouble, and in any case, John was not happy with the stories that told of the sort of Messiah Elijah was to announce. Elijah lived in the days when there was a king in Israel, and John didn't want to start *that* hare running.

'Are you the prophet promised by Moses?'

'No!' This one was easier, although a bit of a surprise. My relative was wandering dangerously close to Samaritan theology here, and his masters in Jerusalem would not be happy to lend any credence to *Samaritan* ideas, which they hated and feared. But clearly, John was not following that line at all.

Several more possible suggestions were made from the whole galaxy of modern speculation, but John would have none of them. He was, after all, an original, and that was what had driven him off to do his own thing in the first place.

My relative was getting desperate.

'Say something, then, I need to write a report on all this,' he pleaded. Very naughty. The rules forbid us to try to get people to compromise themselves.

John was waiting for this. He had the perfect answer ready. Indeed he had used it before.

'I am a voice in the desert! Prepare! He comes!'

No-one could touch him for this. First of all it was a perfectly respectable Biblical text, and it's hard to condemn someone for quoting scripture. Second, it *did* make the claim that the Messiah was just round the corner, and implied that John was his prophet. Third, for those who knew the context, it implied a radical new start both for Jews and for the world at large.

This was enough for my cousin. He could write his report. But there were others with him, no doubt sent as 'minders' by the hard-liners that belonged to our party of reform. They couldn't leave well alone, and asked the next question. It was intended as a put-down, almost a condemnation, but it rebounded.

'Well, if you're just a noise, as useless as the wind in the wilderness, why all the baptisms? You have no status or authority.'

John replied with the core of his message. 'I wash people with water. It prepares them.' (The reformers were big on washing before any significant activity.) 'But washing is not enough. The one who comes will wash your inmost self - he will wash your hearts. He will plunge you into the very Spirit of God's own self.'

John went on, 'You worry about me. If you think I am a matter for all this fuss, then wait. You won't know what has come to you. And you don't have long to wait. He is here. That same Spirit of God that I talk of has shown him to me. He is standing in this gathering. He is God's Chosen One, his son, and I am his witness, and I have now accomplished my task.'

Well, that stopped everything. The reform party got much more than they had bargained for. If they had hoped to silence John, instead they had opened the way for much greater trouble, and they didn't even know whom he was talking about. They had also lost the attention of the crowd. They were all busy looking around at each other, as if one of them was suddenly going to flash out in fire as God's Chosen One. The crowd simply fell apart in a welter of rumour and speculation. Any attempt to discredit John was over, at least for the time being.

What of Andrew and myself? We were just as curious as everyone else, of course. Even among John's immediate group there was no hint of a successor. There was no larger-than-life figure waiting to be announced, and certainly not in such glowing terms. Whom did John mean?

There was no getting near him that day, everyone was mobbing him, but next morning we got our chance.

John was on his way to the river. Apparently his shock announcement didn't mean an end to the baptising. We caught up with him on a bluff just above the bend where the water ran slow and clear; a favourite spot of John's. He was still in his prophetic mode, exalted by the experience of the day before, and images of the Spirit and of the Coming One still tumbled from his lips. We were dying to ask the obvious question, but he gave us no opening, standing there with his legs apart, feet firm planted and a very prophet-like staff in his hand.

Suddenly he ceased, and with a silence as forbidding of conversation as his speaking had been, he raised his staff and levelled it, holding it with one end in his armpit and the other pointing up the hill to the path.

In almost a whisper he declaimed, 'Look. Not a king; a lamb. The Lamb of God!'

He was pointing at Jesus of Nazareth, who had joined us a few days before. Although another Northerner, he was from Nazareth, and Andrew and I had not yet had a conversation with him. He had not struck us in any way as significant until that moment, but he surely did now. He was walking along the path that led gently up, away from the river, and from our bluff we could see his profile. He was looking up the path and towards the hills that come down nearly to the Jordan there. Even though that was the first time I looked at him, really looked at him, that is, I could feel the compact energy, economical and at the same time restless, that was so to impose itself upon my life.

I glanced at Andrew and saw the same thought in his eyes. With a bow to John, still standing like a tree with his staff upraised, we took a sideways route up the hillside, slithering a bit on the rocky patches, as we sought to reach the path along which Jesus was striding.

His pace did not seem particularly energetic, but it was surprising how quickly he was moving, and when we finally stumbled up onto the path itself, he was some way ahead of us. With a quick glance at one another, Andrew and I set off to catch him up.

It took longer than we would have imagined, and Jesus was away from the river valley and part-way to the hills when we came within calling distance. I wasn't too sure what to say, even if I did call, and Andrew was always content to leave the talking to another, and so we simply walked on, gradually closing the gap. Jesus was setting quite a pace.

He must have heard us, eventually, for suddenly he stopped quite still, paused for a moment, and then looked over his shoulder. Seeing us following, he turned full round, stood steadily and firmly right in the middle of the path, and waited for us to come up with him.

We were somewhat out of breath, and so Jesus spoke first. I was relieved at that. However, it was no conventional greeting that he gave, but a direct question.

'What are you searching for that matters so much?'

Maybe better if I *had* spoken first. How could we answer such a question? You can hardly say to a stranger, 'John has just pointed to you as his Messiah, and we wanted to check you out.'

18

I found myself saying lamely, 'Teacher, are you...who are...where are you from? I mean...where are you staying?'

His smile embraced both of us and teased my stuttering. 'You want answers? Come and see.'

I don't propose to tell you what happened that day. It was, and is, the most important day of my life, but also the most private. You may well guess at some of the things shared as I continue the story, because, of course, the changes it made are now part of who I am. I am writing this at least partly so that you may have a similar (but different) encounter of your own, and then you will understand.

Suffice it to say that Andrew and I put roots down there with Jesus and were with him all day; and for many days to come. We had heard John's evidence at his 'trial', but now we were swept into a personal relationship that was built not on hearsay, but on direct encounter. And indeed, our experience did not entirely tally with John's.

For one thing, John had used that curious expression, 'Lamb of God'. It sounded traditional, and it was only when I stopped to think that I realised it has no place in the Bible. It put me in mind of Abraham and Isaac, and also of the Passover, but Jesus was no sacrificial lamb. At least, I thought not at the time. Also, radical and innovative as John was, he did not begin to comprehend just how different Jesus was to be from all our expectations. Even at that first encounter, this began to dawn on us. Here was something, or someone, *really* new.

What does one do in the face of such an experience? I needed time to think, but not our Andrew. Andrew is one of nature's sunny characters. If he has something good, he has to share it. He wants the best for everybody, and that, genuinely and honestly, never begins with himself. His own happiness, about which he never thinks, even in passing, is bound up in the happiness of others.

So off went Andrew as soon as it was light enough to see to find his brother Simon. Simon had come down river to Jericho, about six miles away, on business, and had stopped off a few days ago to see us. I say 'to see us', but much more to see what was going on. He affected to have little time for religion, especially in what he regarded as its rather more extreme forms, but he was curious, nevertheless. I expected Andrew to have some trouble explaining Jesus to Simon.

Andrew was gone all morning and into the afternoon, and I began to think that he had got nowhere with his brother, when I saw the two of them coming up the path towards us. Andrew was bouncing ahead, clearly excited that he had got Simon to journey's end, and the latter was plodding along firmly in his 'I've started, so I'll finish' manner. Jesus and I were sitting outside in the shade of an outcrop of rock, and I was about to nudge Jesus when I realised he was already observing the two with a sharp and thoughtful stare.

Andrew came up first, full of words and explanations, obviously dying for Jesus and Simon to hit it off, but his chatter died away as he realised that no-one was listening to him. No-one was listening to anyone. We were all fully absorbed in looking. Simon was standing to his full height with his feet planted slightly apart in the centre of the path, looking at Jesus with suspicion and reserve. I was watching the outcome with the greatest of interest. Andrew was glancing from face to face in a mixture of hope and apprehension. Jesus seemed both to be gazing firmly at Simon, and at the same time looking inside himself. As I was already learning, these moments of silent communication were the key to recognising Jesus, even though they invariably left one bewildered and dissatisfied.

Then Jesus spoke.

'So you're John's son Simon, are you? Standing there so still and strong.'

He leant back gratefully against our rock, enjoying its

support and shade, and so that the meaning of his next words would be plain to us.

'I need a Rock.'

Whatever Simon had been expecting, it was not this. The name fitted, unexpectedly, but perfectly, and 'Peter' (Rock) he became from that moment. His suspicion and reserve vanished in a flash. Jesus had touched him at one of those hidden springs which we all carry deep within ourselves. No theology, no explanation (Peter was very different from his brother and myself), no appeal to hopes or ideals. Just this:

'I need a Rock.'

The next day we set out for Galilee. Peter needed to be back to sort things out with the business, and I wondered how he would explain to his father John that *another* son was going off in the cause of religion, and this time with someone he had never heard of. But our main reason for going was Jesus' own desire. It seemed strange that he wanted to leave Bethany at once. Why did he not let the Baptist point him out to others among his followers, and indeed to the crowd in general. But Jesus just laughed at the idea.

'I have the three of you, already. I'm not trying to raise an army. We need time together.'

It turned out that Jesus had a family wedding to go to, in Cana, and he intended to travel via Nazareth from where he would finish the journey with his mother and brothers. We were to join him there after we had returned to Bethsaida and seen our own families.

We travelled up the Jordan valley, sleeping rough the first night, and spending the second night in Scythopolis, the main city of the Decapolis. It was here that we discovered that Jesus was an inveterate sightseer, especially of temples and other religious buildings.

Scythopolis, according to the Gentiles, had been founded by their god of Wine, Dionysus (indeed the city had been called Nysa in his honour for a time) and Jesus took a special interest in the temples built to this god in the new city at the foot of the tel. (A tel is a mound or hill upon which so many of our older cities were built.)

Jesus himself loved a beaker of wine or two, and that evening he told us some pagan stories attached to the name of the god of the city, mainly to do with his feasts and with his outpouring of wine on his followers at the slightest opportunity. These stories seemed strange on the lips of a Jewish rabbi-teacher, but then, in the traditional sense, Jesus was not a rabbi. He taught in his own way, using the most unexpected material and images, and we loved it.

It was on this journey also that we began to discover Jesus' love for words and word-play. His naming of Peter was typical of this, and he would often take a word and re-use it in a new and surprising context, or make a pun of it, or take a careless or conventional phrase and restore to it its original force. It was at this time that he nicknamed me 'Beloved', which is as much of the literal meaning of my name that a good Jew can say out loud.

We parted there, and two days later met again at Cana.

While Andrew, Peter and I had been in Bethsaida, we had run into an old acquaintance in the shape of Philip, who it transpired was invited to the same wedding as Jesus. We walked together up the Valley of the Doves to Cana. This is a lovely walk, and we were to do it often. As you leave the lakeside at Magdala there is a narrow valley with the Heights of Arbel towering over you on the south side. You pass the caves where the last Herod (the present Herod's father) went 'fishing for men' - lowering soldiers on ropes to pull the defenders out of the caves with grappling hooks. There are veterans still alive who are only too ready to tell you the story. This is by far the easiest ascent up onto the plain to the north of Nazareth. When you reach the plain, it is fertile and well-cultivated, and the walk is more-or-less on the level (rare for Galilee!) until you reach the Tel of Cana tucked beneath the northern hills that rim the plain. Nazareth is across the valley to the south; about eight or nine miles away.

We pitched camp on the top of the tel, not far from the southern gate, and near a convenient water cistern, of which Cana has many. Philip had left us; he had the offer of a bed in the town. When we were settled in, we went to find Jesus. Only two days away from him, and we were dying to renew the relationship so suddenly begun at Bethany. Jesus, we knew, would have arrived in the morning, with his family.

In fact, we only made it as far as the gate, at which point we met Jesus, who was coming in search of us. He was as keen to continue what we'd started as we were. But Jesus was not alone. He had his arm round Philip's neck, and they were laughing together as they came towards us.

'Look whom I've discovered,' said Jesus, 'And what a discovery!'

'So this is your bright hope,' said Philip, still laughing at whatever he and Jesus had been sharing together, 'I begin to understand.'

It turned out that Philip too had been reading and pondering the Messianism that was so much in the air at the moment, and he had a good friend here in Cana, indeed his host for the wedding period, with whom he shared and discussed these things. He now wanted above all to go and tell him about Jesus. His friend was something of a Bible scholar.

I asked to go with him. I was curious as to how someone clearly much more traditional than Andrew or I would take Philip's announcement. The others went back to our encampment to begin preparing the evening meal. Jesus went with them, rather than return to his family; his brothers were not the easiest of people, and his mother was fully engaged in the women's world of 'wedding coming soon'.

Philip led me to the house of his friend Nathaniel, which, unusually for Cana, had a small atrium with a fig-tree in the centre and flowers and herbs in pots around the sides and along the five-foot wall that separated the courtyard from the street. It was a cool and refreshing place, and Nathaniel was taking his ease on a folding stool under the tree, with a beaker of wine at his side and a book on his knee. His arm rested carelessly across the book, to keep the scrolls apart, but he was clearly not reading. He was miles away, looking out across the valley through the open gate, on some journey of the mind.

Philip usually had perfect manners, but he stood on no ceremony with his friend, or perhaps he was more stirred and excited than he showed. He gave no greeting, nor did he introduce us, he simply launched into his news.

'We have discovered him. The one promised in the Bible. He's come. He's here in Cana.'

Nathaniel looked at his friend. Various emotions chased across his face. He glanced at me, wondering if we had been drinking. He looked back at Philip wondering if he'd had too much sun on the walk. A flicker of hope was followed by a look of resignation. How many hares had been started, especially in Galilee, only to come to nothing? His silence stirred Philip into further speech.

'He is here. It is Jesus, from Nazareth, the son of Joseph.'

Just as Nathaniel feared - another false dawn. He glanced down at his book, clearly one of the scriptures, and looked out across the valley where you could just see the top few houses of Nazareth before it disappeared over the far slope of the hill. He looked across at Sepphoris, Herod's shining new city which this same Joseph had helped to build, and which was again the capital, eclipsing the second-rate Nazareth beyond.

'Nazareth?' he said, 'Hardly!'

I could sympathise with him. As a native of Cana, a beautiful and a rather (dare I say) snobbish town, set on its own tel rather than sprawling down a hillside, he would have his prejudices against work-a-day Nazareth. As a scholar, he would know that there is no mention of Nazareth anywhere in the Bible, still less in the Messianic prophecies. As a cultured and interested student of current affairs, he would know how many times just this sort of statement had been made, only to end in tears, and in some cases even in the horrible Roman crosses stretched across the landscape.

Philip knew better than to argue. He himself had been totally bored by our talk of Jesus as we walked from Bethsaida earlier.

'Come and see', he said.

Nathaniel was not keen. He looked resignedly at his unfinished wine, and then glanced at the shadows beginning to rise up the east wall of his courtyard. Clearly it would be too dark to continue reading by the time he had extricated himself from Philip's obsession. But his manners won. After all, he was Philip's host, and the duties of hospitality certainly included going with his guest to meet a friend. He called for someone to come and take his book and stool inside, and, too courteous to drain it in front of us, carefully perched his beaker in a convenient crotch in his fig-tree. He slipped on his sandals, and stepped outside with us to walk to the camp.

We came to Jesus, who was sitting outside our tent, gazing at the same view that had prompted Nathaniel's condemnation of Nazareth. Jesus, no doubt, had accompanied his father many times on the road between Nazareth and Sepphoris, during the building of the latter, and knew this valley well. He sensed our approach, and turned his head to look directly at Nathaniel. I had begun to understand the way he did things, and waited for the impossible remark that would be totally apt. I don't think Nathaniel had realised yet that this was the man.

'So, do come too! As true a Jew as ever I knew!'

I thought Jesus had blown it this time. Nathaniel was not one for word-play and rhymes, and he was already convinced that Jesus could not be the one, and this was hardly the level of seriousness that he would expect of God's anointed. But again,

Jesus was right. The last thing Nathaniel wanted was another yard of the same. Serious and devout himself, he was well aware that more was needed. And, true to form, he had listened to the *meaning* of what Jesus had said. He heard both the invitation and the assessment of his own character. Being indeed true and honest, he didn't think to disclaim or go in for false modesty. He knew himself. But how did Jesus?

Straight out, Nathaniel asked him. 'How do *you* know that?'

'I saw you,' said Jesus, 'long before Philip came for you. You were under your fig-tree.'

It all made sense, even to me. The others were looking puzzled, including Philip, but I had seen enough to know what that fig-tree meant to Nathaniel. It was his place of study, his place of rest, and his place of struggle. He *was* true. True to his search. True in his prayers. True to the long great Jewish tradition of wrestling with God. His tree was the symbol for Nathaniel of this, *and Jesus knew it*. In his life-long wrestling match, Nathaniel had just taken his first fall, and he was aware of himself enough to know with whom he wrestled, and who alone could throw him. He acknowledged his fall at once.

'You, teacher, are God's son, true king of the kingdom.'

The phrases were messianic, of course, and I already knew that Jesus had his own way of interpreting them, but he accepted Nathaniel's passionate offering as it was meant, and again, seeing the striving and longing within him, went further than with any of us. He smiled a smile of compassion, tinged a little with the sadness of knowledge, as he often would when speaking prophetically.

'Because I know of your dreams, wrestler? You shall see more. Remember our founding-father Jacob, who wrestled with God? Remember his dream?' With this he rose slowly to his feet, the setting sun catching him full in the face as he stood. He spoke again and to us all.

'Hear then the word of truth. You shall see the marrying of earth and of heaven, of time and of the eternal, of the world as you see it, and of the world as it truly is. This you will see in me.'

Chapter 3

'Have you any idea what it is that I have just done for you?' Jesus asked from his place on the couch between Judas and myself.

To be honest, we hadn't. Each of us had had a moment with Jesus - a moment of communion and inward truth, but clearly he meant much more than that.

'You call me your teacher, even your master. Rightly. I am. If I, teacher, master, can wash your feet, then you can do it for one another. Love is about serving, and serving is nothing to do with 'greater' or 'menial'. Love is above these things.'

He paused, and his prophetic smile hovered again on his lips as the familiar opening rang out.

'Hear then the word of truth. Nothing done by love can degrade you. Although I shall be humiliated by what is coming, I do it in love, and therefore am exalted, not degraded. As this is true of me, so it is of you. God is the source of love, of me and of you. Love unites us.'

He paused for this to sink in, and I felt him shiver as the trouble I had seen earlier in his eyes again surged through him.

'I was not humbled by washing your feet. If you felt it as an insult to me, then know that love does not work so. If however you felt insulted by me, then love did not touch you. I know you all, and one of you does indeed reject this gift of life. He has eaten my bread - The Bread - and is nevertheless against me.'

Jesus was trembling even more violently as he said this, and I twisted in alarm to look up at his face; not easy from my position leaning against him. Over his shoulder I could see Judas' face, more dark and closed than ever, and well knew that he was taking all this most personally. He thought Jesus meant him, and in truth, I thought the same. He felt Jesus was trying to insult him further, and was not hearing the words of love, only the challenge of attack.

Jesus had more to say.

'You should know what is about to happen, and I warn you now to prepare you. Whatever evil is done to me will exalt me, for I accept it for the sake of love. I open my arms to the world.'

And again the powerful prophetic introduction: 'Hear then the word of truth. Open your arms. Love links all who love. All who open themselves to you are open to me. All who are open to me are open to God.'

Again the trembling surged through his body, and again the words of prophecy; I had never heard him use them so often, so closely before.

'Hear then the word of truth. One of you is closed to me, and closed to love. He will hand me over to those who seek my death.'

Each time he returned to this theme, the meaning became plainer. People were looking about and at each other. They were looking for the traitor in just the way that the Baptist's crowd had looked for the Messiah. The incongruity hit me as I saw in them the same curiosity, the same lack of awareness of the real significance, the same sense of it being important, yes, but not about their very being. I guessed, of course, what Jesus meant, but I was uncomfortably aware that my own heart was not clean. I had not accepted Jesus washing my feet in the spirit he had indicated, and nor, I suspect had any, unless it were the two Marys. I felt the lack of understanding in the room swell out from his hearers and roll towards Jesus.

Peter was gesturing to me from half-way down the right-hand couch. 'Who?', he mouthed, 'Who?', and with a crosswise jerk of his forefinger he indicated that I should ask Jesus.

I wanted to say, 'It's you, Peter, and me. Don't you see?'

but there was no way I could begin to explain across the couches, and neither Peter, nor anyone, was particularly receptive at that moment. Nor was I thinking anywhere near as coherently as it seems when I set it on paper.

I leant back against Jesus, feeling the pounding of his heart against my head.

'Who?' I asked, indicating Peter's questioning face on the one hand, and with a glance over Jesus' shoulder at Judas on the other.

'Watch', said Jesus.

He took a piece of the pan-bread in front of him. (This was the last day we could eat ordinary bread before the whole house was scoured clean of any trace of yeast as the eight-day 'Feast of Unleavened Bread', the 'Passover' began. The women had baked a whole pan-bread for each of us as a treat.) Jesus opened the bit he had torn off to make a little wallet, and dipping in the chicken and herb goulash in front of him, found a particularly nice piece of breast, put it in the bread, and handed the packet to Judas.

This is a sign of honour and respect at one of our feasts. It has particular meaning at the Passover, which was to begin the next evening, but is often done at the Sabbath feast, and at a formal dinner. Jesus was making another attempt to show Judas that he had not been insulting him. This was a mark of high regard. (I am delighted to say that it didn't even cross my mind that reclining as I was on Jesus' right hand, this honour was due to me. Perhaps I was learning.)

Judas took it. He looked at Jesus, and for a moment his dark anger seemed to lift a bit. Was there even a spark of hope in his eyes? Then, as he swallowed, his face darkened again. He looked at Jesus as if Jesus was trying to trick him with his gift. I read a moment of despair in his eyes, and as he caught me looking at him the anger welled up and the shutters came down. I feel to this day a part of that moment. Did the fact that I was watching seal him in his decision? Might he have changed his mind, otherwise? Whether or not, that exchange of looks binds me into what he did. Forgiven, of course, and free of it; nevertheless, it is good that I do not forget.

'Then do it. Do it now. Get it over,' said Jesus.

Judas slid backward from the couch, found his feet, avoiding Jesus' eye as he pulled his cloak round him, and slipped quietly around the side of the room to the door. A few noticed his going, but made nothing of it. They could not hear the conversation on the top table, although Peter, who had clearly followed some of the body language, was looking both thoughtful and bewildered. No doubt they thought that Judas was off on some duty as treasurer; to buy for the Passover, or give some of the so-called 'second tithe' to the needy, as our Law requires.

Judas opened the door, still avoiding anyone's eye, and looked out into the darkness outside. It seemed to reach forward to swallow him, darker even than his own dark mood, and he was gone. Joseph pushed the door shut with his foot, blotting out the square of blackness, but I could still see it, cold, in my mind.

The contrast made the room seem brighter, warmer, and our fellowship more precious, here in this island of light with the dark outside surrounding us. Jesus felt this, too, for his tone changed as he moved over on the couch a little, part-covering the now-empty place of Judas, and giving us both more room. The talk was still of betrayal and failure, especially of failing to live up to Jesus. Into the heart of this he spoke again.

'I spoke of being exalted; indeed I shall be covered in glory within a short time. This is my moment, it has come at last.'

All conversation stopped again. Jesus was doing that a lot, this night.

'It will seem shameful, but in truth it will be glory. God's glory is God's, not to be recognised unless you look beneath the surface of things. This is my moment, and I shall be leaving you. You can follow me no longer.

'But if you wish to be my follower, then I have a new command. You know the Law; love God; love your neighbour. My new command is "Love one another!"

'Does this seem easy? I tell you it is harder than the rest. You know each other too well. If you can do this thing, you will find that indeed you do love God; that you can love your neighbour. If you can do this thing, you will indeed be following me, even if I am no longer with you.'

Jesus has a gift for packing a lot into a very few words. Different ones of us were clearly grappling with different parts of this pronouncement.

Thomas, always quick to see the political implications, was picking up on public shame. He had always said it would end this way, and he didn't like Jesus' talk of 'exaltation', which was very close to the Roman slang for 'crucifixion'. Joseph, too, with his knowledge of the ploys of power and the plans of our politicians, was looking uncomfortable at this. He, of all of us, knew how close Jesus had been sailing to the wind. We had heard through him and others of several attempts by the Council either to arrest Jesus or to have him lynched.

Martha and Mary of Magdala were digesting the implications of the command to 'love one another'. They were quick to pick up the hints of how hard this would be compared with the traditional commands, and I could see they were breaking it down into practicalities in their minds.

Martha's Mary was looking stricken, and no doubt was wondering how literally Jesus was talking about dying. This had been on her mind for the last few days, after she had washed Jesus' feet and he had spoken of her helping to bury him.

Peter had picked up on not being able to follow Jesus. Probably he hadn't really heard the rest, for which I couldn't blame him. He had only been able to catch onto fragments of the whole Judas episode, and the questioning of anyone's loyalty Peter would take most seriously. He stumbled rather with Jesus' higher flights of theology, and most of Jesus' flights were deceptively high, but Peter did understand steadfastness, and courage, and loyalty. He was indeed our 'Rock'. As usual, he did his thinking out loud.

'Master, where do you say you are going?'

'I'm sorry, Peter, this is something I do alone. You cannot come with me on this road. At least, not yet a while,' replied Jesus.

'Why not now?' persisted Peter, 'Even if the road leads to death, I will walk it with you. You know I would willingly die for you.'

This we all knew to be a fact. Anyone who knew Peter even a little would have agreed that he only spoke the sober truth. Jesus knew him better than any, knew his full-hearted loyalty and love for his Master, and so his next statement came as a total bolt from the blue.

'Die for me? The cock will herald the dawn in less than eight hours. Before then you will have disowned me. Not once, not twice, but three times.'

Chapter 4

I shall leave the Upper Room again to go back to another time when Jesus had his back to the ropes. This was by the Sea of Galilee. It seems appropriate to interrupt the main story here, with a tale that shows Peter's support and loyalty to Jesus, and explains just what a shock Jesus' accusation of abandonment was. You will have to be patient however; Peter's part comes at the end of quite a long story.

We need to go back almost exactly a year from the Upper Room, when again, it was nearly time for the Passover-feast of unleavened bread.

The Passover is our main feast of the year, and remembers when we were slaves in Egypt, bitterly oppressed, and God persuaded Moses (not without some difficulty) to go to Pharaoh, the king of Egypt, to demand our release. Not unnaturally, Pharaoh didn't want to lose all that free labour, and refused. Egypt was then subject to a series of plagues until Pharaoh changed his mind. The last and greatest plague killed all the first-born, but 'passed over' the people of Israel. We were then able to flee from Egypt, but in such a hurry that we had only time to bake unleavened bread - we couldn't wait for the ordinary kind to 'rise'. Pharaoh pursued us with his army, but God opened a way for us through the Red Sea, and so we escaped. We then wandered in the wilderness for many years, until God gave us the land we now live in. During the wilderness years, God fed us with special bread called 'manna' that came from heaven. You will find many of the themes of this story, our defining story as a nation, crop up in what I am about to tell you.

This story begins on a grassy hill on the far side of the Sea of Galilee, in the area under the jurisdiction of Philip, brother of Herod, and a rather safer place at that time for religious leaders than was Galilee. I say this because our former master John had recently been imprisoned and beheaded by Herod, in part at least because Herod was frightened of his popularity.

There is a valley that leads up into the hills about five miles south of Bethsaida down the eastern shore, and about a mile and a half up this valley is the knoll to which I refer.

Jesus was at the height of his popularity with the crowds, and thousands of them, so it seemed, had materialised from nowhere to see and hear him. Most were from the towns of the lakeside, but not a few were from the surrounding hills. These latter were a fairly dissident bunch who also preferred the safety of Philip's territory, or of the Decapolis, the border of which was only a couple of miles further south. Nor surprisingly, in these circumstances, they were predominantly male, but not all, as we shall see.

This was not an area where markets abounded, and so Jesus raised the question of food. Specifically, he asked Philip where we could buy loaves for the crowd. Jesus was teasing Philip, as Bethsaida was at least six miles away, and Susita as far to the south across the border.

Philip, however, took the question at face value, and after a few mental sums said that we'd need at least 200 denarii - a quite impossible amount as a denarius was the average daily wage in the countryside. It was a bit literal-minded of Philip, and you will notice that it wasn't an answer to the question that Jesus had asked, which was 'where', not 'how much'. Actually, Jesus never displayed the slightest interest in money, at least in terms of how much or how little we had in our shared fund.

Andrew overheard, and he had a better answer. He had been chatting with a young lady of about thirteen who was there with her family's picnic. She was feeling very proud and adult, and had been making her way to get as close to the centre of events as possible. Andrew looked up from where he was sitting next to her, and said, 'There's a young one here with a lunch of barley loaves and cooked fish.'

She promptly opened her bag to display them and Andrew did a rapid inventory.

'Five of the first and two of the second,' he amplified, 'But you'll have to spread them thin in this crowd!'

'Just so,' said Jesus, 'Make everybody sit down.'

He turned to the girl. 'You don't mind sharing?' he asked.

She seemed apprehensive at this, whether because Jesus himself was speaking to her, or at the prospect of losing the family lunch, but she looked back at him with big round eyes, shook her head and held out the open bag to Jesus. She then with all the dignity of her thirteen self-conscious years sat down again next to Andrew, whom she clearly regarded as much safer than Jesus, although she would die rather than admit it.

Meanwhile we had been trying to get everybody to sit down. Not as easy as you might think, because we had no idea what was going to happen next, and we were making no promises and trying to arouse no expectations. In this, of course, we failed totally, as the very request set off all sorts of suggestions and speculations.

When at least those round about had sat down, and Jesus could be seen and heard again, he stood up (he had been sitting to teach, as was the custom). He took the loaves, and said grace, and broke them, and started giving out great handfuls to those nearest to him. The strange thing was, the more he gave, the more he seemed to have in his hands. It soon seemed as if he had not his hands, but his arms full of fragments of the barley bread. He continued to dole out generous portions from what seemed an inexhaustible supply.

Gradually people began to realise what was happening, and a buzz of speculation arose, but a sort of hushed buzz. People realised that they were the privileged witnesses of something very special. Some tasted the bread suspiciously, as if it would disappear in their mouths, or give no nourishment. Others seemed frightened to try it at all. Yet others, realising they were receiving a free meal, started to eat as rapidly as they could in the hope of more.

Jesus turned to us after he had shared with a few dozen, and said in the most down-to-earth way, 'Here. You do this, I need to do something about that fish.' He shoved a pile of bread into Andrew's arms, more into Philip's, and suddenly we were all moving among the people with bread and to spare.

Meanwhile Jesus had taken the two fish - a local delicacy from Magdala, across the water, where they are smoked in the famous tower that gives Magdala ('Curing Tower') its name. He blessed and broke the fish in the same way as he had the bread, and a second wave of sharing was following the first.

There were plenty of us to help, fortunately. As I said, Jesus was at the height of his popularity, and the numbers of actual disciples (by that I mean men and women who were travelling with us and sharing our common life) was greater than at any time before or since. Even so, the task took some time, and the eating took even longer. We were only able ourselves to eat by grabbing quick mouthfuls of what we were sharing out.

But the task was not over. No sooner than we had satisfied even those who were chasing a third or fourth helping, Jesus had another job for us.

'Take our baskets,' he said. 'Borrow some if necessary. Gather up anything left over. It's very important that we don't lose anything.'

In the ordinary way, this was not like Jesus. He was prodigal with food, and lived entirely from day to day. Others might worry about it if they wished, but he felt it an unnecessary waste of energy that could be used in enjoying life. I wondered for a moment if he felt there was something sacred about the bread and fish, but put that thought aside as even less likely than Jesus suddenly having a fit of thrift.

We began to do as he said, and brought the leftovers to his feet, filling our own baskets, and having to borrow more. As we did this, it began to dawn on me that this was another of what Jesus called his 'signs', like the wedding at Cana which I shall tell you about later, and like the foot-washing which you already know about.

To this day I have never been able quite to put into words what Jesus meant by 'sign'; I suppose if it could be reduced to words it would make the action unnecessary. The best I can do is to say that they were moments when Jesus took the things of this world and made them open up a window into the world of eternity. They were not symbolic actions, although laden with symbolism, and Jesus didn't like it when people tried to interpret them symbolically. They were moments when the hiddenness of God broke though into the open, but even then, only for those who wanted to see it that way. There were many present who didn't, and the signs in no way compelled or even encouraged belief either in Jesus or in his source. Rather, they opened up new dimensions of what it meant to live both here and in eternity at the same time, and for the two to be one. In order to see that, you needed to be thinking along these lines already.

So the gathering up was all a part of the sign. We gathered no less than twelve baskets of left-overs.

Of course, everybody was talking about what had just happened. Now the moment a group of Jews start discussing anything like this, out come the Bibles, metaphorically speaking. By that I mean we all carry large parts of the Bible around in our heads and in our hearts.

Some were remembering the times when Elijah and Elisha fed people miraculously, while others were even comparing Jesus to Moses, who was responsible for the manna in the wilderness at the time of our wanderings. In the current climate, and particularly in that part of the world, this led straight to the expected Messiah. Moses had promised another prophet like himself, and that promise was very much alive in the thinking of the day, particularly among the Samaritans, but also among us Jews. You will remember that my relative had asked John about this. People full from the bread Jesus had just given them, and from the excitement of what they had just witnessed, were making this link, and asking if Jesus could possibly be that prophet.

But there was another strand of thinking going on in parts of the crowd. In our generation religion and politics were two sides of the same coin; indeed for many, and for many in this particular gathering, they *were* the same thing. There were quite a few there who, once the word 'Messiah' was in the air, took off into their own political visions. These were the dissidents from the hills around (with not a few of the lake-siders in full sympathy) who wanted an armed rebellion against Rome, or against our collaborationist aristocracy, or against both, or simply to overturn the existing order and start a new world. There were a dozen different agendas at work. 'Messiah' to them meant 'king', or 'warrior' or 'liberator'. Jesus, by doing a clearly messianic deed, was good enough for them.

Talk was rising about a new rebellion, with Jesus at its head. None of these hotheads, of course, thought to consult Jesus on this. They all were sure *they* knew what to do; *he* would just fit into their plans. This was exactly what had made Nathaniel so suspicious when Philip first told him about Jesus.

The crowd seemed to be turning into a rabble, and from that it was only a short step to a 'people's army', and Jesus was entirely vulnerable to their will. He realised what was happening as soon as anybody, and that the whole thing was well out of hand.

'I'm taking to the hills,' he said to us, urgency vibrating in his sudden whisper. 'Take the boats back to Capernaum. I'll meet you when I can.'

'I'll go with you,' said Peter, 'You're going to need my

help.' (By which Peter meant 'protection'.) He looked round to see if others of us would go too.

'No,' said Jesus, still in a desperate undertone, for Peter had been overheard by some of those near by. 'This is a time for flight, not fight. I'm a hillsman; I'll do better on my own.'

This was plainly true. Jesus was lithe and fit, and had lived most of his life in the hills of Galilee. Peter, well-built as he was, could by no means move as fast as Jesus, and the more that went with him, the slower and more obvious the party would be. In any case, the king-makers would not expect Jesus to go off without his disciples.

So Jesus slipped away east, down off the back of our knoll and up into the Golan Heights. Meanwhile, we made our presence as obvious as we could, moving among the people and joining in the talk where possible. As ever with politics, there had to be a great deal of discussion before anyone was ready to stir into action, if that time was to come at all. Andrew bore off his teenager to reunite her with her family, wherever they had got to in the crowd.

Gradually it dawned on people that Jesus was not there, and there was quite a bit of anger expressed. I date it from this moment that his popularity began to slide. For a time I thought that things could turn ugly for us. With no Jesus we were an obvious target for the anger, and we were concerned to get our womenfolk away down the valley and to the boats. Philip and Andrew, knowing the country as they did, managed this quietly and competently.

Fortunately it was getting late in the day, and the more sober citizens, especially those whose homes were across the lake in Herod's jurisdiction, began to feel quite relieved that the rebellion seemed to be postponed, if not over before it had begun. Moods began to change, and people drifted off. Jesus was well away by now, and we felt that we too could slip off down to the lakeside.

Andrew and Philip had left us a boat, and Mary of Magdala

had stayed behind to guard it. She was sitting watchfully in the bows and fending off would-be passengers, of which there were several, as quite a few lake-siders had been caught by the sunset with no means of crossing over. Being from Magdala, Mary knew many of these, and was far better able to deal with them than most of us, and of course she was another of our band who knew how to handle a boat.

There were eight of us left, in addition to Mary, and the boat was low in the water as we pushed off and made for Capernaum, six miles away to the north-west. People were watching us, and I was glad that they could see that Jesus was not with us. The less known about his movements the better.

It was already getting dark, and we knew it would be full night before we came to Capernaum, and so Peter decided that we should sail north around the shore, rather than strike out in a straight line.

We had the sail up, partly for the sake of speed, and partly because it was heavy work rowing a boat so laden and low in the water, but Peter was not happy. He kept glancing across at the shore, especially when we came opposite the valley leading up to Gamla. I knew why. The wind was irregular, and sudden squalls could come gusting down all in a moment out of these wadis.

Indeed, Peter's instinct was right, and he suddenly lurched across from the steering oar and unloosed the halyard, shouting as he did, ''Ware sail!'

There was a scurrying in the centre of the boat as we all leapt out of the way of the falling yard and its cumbersome sail, and out of the corner of my eye I caught what Peter had seen; a patch of dark and broken water sweeping toward us from the shore, tell-tale of the squall above it.

Peter's prompt action meant that we were no more than pushed by the wind, shipping perhaps a basketful of water, soon bailed out, but in all likelihood there was more on the way.

'Out oars!' commanded Peter, and the seamen among us (I

was one) obeyed. 'Give way, Starboard! Back Port!' called Peter, twisting the steering oar for all it was worth, and we came slowly round, with our bows pointing no longer parallel to the shore towards Bethsaida (from when we would have worked round to our destination), but instead out into the centre of the lake.

Peter had two reasons. The first, and most immediate was to get us stern on to the next squall, instead of presenting our vulnerable beam to it, and indeed, as we swung, the next flurry struck us. His second reason was that, against expectation, we knew we should be safer out to sea (or, at least, as far out to sea as you can get when the other side is only seven miles away). This is because these squalls, whistling suddenly down a wadi, push up waves, and these interact with each other, bouncing off the shore, and are at their worst where the sea is shallow. Out in the middle it would be cold and wet, but much less dangerous.

We rowed hard to put some distance between us and the shore, pursued by further flurries, shipping some water from the squalls, and some from our splashy rowing. It was hard to keep a stroke with the boat lurching erratically. We set our landsmen to bail. I couldn't see their complexions, but I guessed some of them were green, and perhaps they were regretting their smoked fish - whatever the source. They were also dismayed to see the land retreating, and didn't have the confidence we might have liked in our explanations.

We were now out in the sea, somewhere in the middle, but with only the vaguest idea where, because no land was in sight; no glimmer of a light from any of the shore-side settlements. The wind had stirred up the warm sea and raised its usual haze.

'Easy!' ordered Peter, and we gratefully rested on our oars. 'Just the odd stroke, now,' he added, 'enough to keep her tail to the wind.' He had clearly decided to wait out the night in the safety of the middle of the lake, and to make for shore in daylight.

Leaning on my oar, letting it rest on my chest, with my arms over it, and dipping and pulling occasionally, I looked around at the curtain of night that seemed about fifteen yards from the boat. Suddenly I thought I saw a loom in the dark; a piece of slightly more solid darkness that seemed to be moving nearer. Others must have been looking in the same direction too, for several cried out and pointed.

Whatever it was (and I knew of no phenomenon like it on the lake) became more solid, and all at once looked human-shaped; but on the deep water. The tingle of the supernatural started in my stomach, ran up my spine, and lodged itself at the nape of my neck. Even Peter allowed himself a gasp of surprise and fear. Someone, I don't remember who, began to recite Psalm 7, a psalm for deliverance from evil.

My one thought was an overwhelming wish that Jesus were here. I felt this so strongly that I could actually hear his voice.

'I am! Do not be afraid!'

And then I realised that I *could* hear him. It wasn't a voice in my head; it was real. It was clear that the others could hear him too. The tension burst like a bubble. There was laughter, high and overdone in reaction. Someone came out with a line from Psalm 107 (about saving those in peril on the sea). Peter was grinning as if his face would split.

Jesus came up to us, climbed into the boat, and (no waiting for dawn) in no time at all we were rocking on a mooring at Capernaum.

It happened so quickly, and we were in so much distress, that it was only afterwards, when I replayed it in my mind, that I noticed what Jesus had actually said.

'I am! Do not be afraid!'

I suppose I had heard it initially as a response for my deep longing for him to be there, and taken it to mean 'I am here', but neither I, nor any of us had asked the question, at least not out loud. It was not an answer. It was an announcement.

'I am' has a special meaning for us Jews. It is the name of God (or close to it) that he revealed to Moses at the time just before our deliverance from slavery. The proper name of God, which we never say or write, is a form of the verb 'I am' that has meaning in past, present and future. Jesus, just saying 'I am' like that was coming very close to claiming that the divine name was his own.

When I think back, and knowing how Jesus used 'I am' with precisely this meaning in his trials by the authorities and in his battles with the reform party, I am sure that the implication was there as he walked toward us on the face of the water. He was contrasting his view of what it meant to be Messiah from the mistaken and dangerous views of the revolutionaries earlier in the day. He was quite specifically claiming a oneness with the Creator (whose Spirit moved on the water at the beginning of things) and contrasting that with any merely human notions of kingship and power, however grandiose.

Essentially, the power to create is the opposite of any power that is based on force, or fear, or control of others. It also makes any other power seem very secondary and insignificant. (I suspect that giving birth, or even the inherent possibility within one, makes the truth of this real and personal; which is perhaps why women don't need to run after power and authority in quite the same way that men so often have to.) Peter was good at control in the first sense; look at how he had taken over in the emergency on the lake, where he had indeed been our 'Rock'. But it did make it hard for him to understand the sort of power Jesus was concerned with, and learning this was a slow and painful road for Peter.

The next day was Friday, and we awoke (late, as you might expect, after the excitements of the day before and of the night) to find the whole lake a-buzz with movement.

Word had travelled all round the shore telling a range of versions of what had happened at Jesus' meal. We were glad to see that this, rather than the failed king-making, was the centre of interest. Acute boat owners, especially from Tiberias, which had the largest fleet, were out across the lake chaffering with those stranded on the other side, and offering them passage across. Everyone wanted to get to Capernaum, where Jesus was due to preach the late-afternoon sermon that would prepare people for the Sabbath, which begins at sunset on Friday.

He had been asked a while ago by the synagogue authorities, who at this stage in the proceedings were wondering what they had let themselves in for. You would think the more that people are religious, the more that they would be open to the unexpected, considering that unexpectedness is the one predictable thing about God; but the rule seems to be that the more apparently pious become less open to change. It is very sad, and Jesus often had things to say about it.

The other question, before he made his appearance - he was no exception in the sleeping-in stakes - was concerning his whereabouts. People knew that we had taken our last boat the evening before, and that he was not in it. If he was still on the other side of the sea, how could he keep his engagement? The synagogue leaders brightened perceptibly at this thought.

Jesus did not show himself until just before time for prayers. He was tired out after his long walk in the hills - he had been up nearly as far as Gamla and down the same valley that produced our freak winds - and he was also in a fey mood. The experiences of yesterday had left a strong sense with him that he had not been clear enough in his message. Perhaps, he felt, he had been bending over too far to make things easy for people, and so it was his fault that they had sprung to facile conclusions. I suspect another reason for his staying hidden was that he was amused by the speculation, and wasn't going to end it before the dramatically right moment.

Not long before the tenth hour (two hours before sunset) he made his way to the synagogue, which is set back a bit from the shore, and only just over a block away from the house that Peter and Andrew keep in Capernaum, where we were staying. The synagogue is a simple one, and there are plans to replace it, but it has the advantage of three doors at the shore-ward end, and of large windows, so that many more can hear than those actually squashed inside.

As soon as Jesus approached, he was pounced on by those who had hitched lifts in the Tiberias boats.

'Teacher, when did you arrive?'

'We thought you across the sea.'

'How did you get here?'

To this last Jesus gave the laconic reply, 'Walked!' and I caught the slightest flicker of a wink at Mary, who with the other women of our band was about to slip away through the crush into the women's side of the synagogue. The reply didn't satisfy people, and Jesus found that he would have to say something more if he was to have any chance of pushing his way through to the teaching-chair. Over the heads of the crowd inside we could see the synagogue steward for the day bobbing up and down anxiously looking for the preacher. Jesus had to give them more, and as usual, he answered less the questions on their lips, and more the thoughts in their hearts.

'Hear then the word of truth;' (that smile was on his lips again) 'You ate bread and were full, and think it wonderful. You failed to see beyond the bread. Don't go chasing dead bread. You will be hungry again tomorrow. Come and listen, and I will tell you about God's own bread. Be open to what I can give you. Indeed, it comes from God, whose ambassador I am.'

People, not surprisingly, looked puzzled and a little hurt at this, but they made a way for him to get through, and some of us were lucky enough to slip through in his wake. Whether Jesus had intended it or not, he couldn't have given a better trailer for his sermon.

A good sermon can be the most exciting thing on earth; as entertainment, as food for thought, as interaction between preacher and hearers, as a sharing, almost a uniting in a transcendent solidarity. Jesus' sermons were often better even than that.

The main reading for the day is always taken from the Law, and with the Passover approaching, the appointed reading was the story in Exodus when Moses (or rather God) provides manna in the wilderness. We had also sung Psalm 78, which talks of the same story in terms of God giving us bread from heaven to eat. There was another reading from the prophets, which I shall mention later, and after this it was Jesus' turn.

It is traditional for someone to ask a question, to get things going, usually based on a text taken from the psalm or main reading. The steward for the day, still clearly very nervous and wanting to avoid all controversy, decided to play safe and ask the question himself. It was about as bland as you can get.

'How should we behave in order to please God?' he asked. 'What should we do?'

'If you want to please God,' said Jesus, 'believe in his ambassador.'

Everybody in the synagogue and all those listening at the doors and windows knew he meant himself, of course, even if they hadn't heard his statement on the steps outside. The steward looked helpless, and someone near the front called out the next question, before the poor man had time to say something else weak and ineffectual.

'What are your credentials, then?' the new questioner asked, 'We need some evidence.' Then, with the readings fresh in our minds, the questioner continued, 'Moses gave us bread in the wilderness, and we have just sung "He gave them bread from heaven to eat."'

I saw Jesus' eyes glint. This question was a gift. I thought in passing of the feeding of the crowd the day before, and was amused that the questioner obviously had not been there, or had not made the messianic deductions that so many of them had. Otherwise he would not be asking for a sign like Moses' manna; which was just what Jesus had in fact done.

Now that he had his text, which was much along the lines he had prepared, Jesus launched into the sermon. The first few minutes set the context of the story, and corrected the common shorthand by pointing out that not Moses, but God was responsible for the manna. He then went on to explain that God still gives bread from heaven, even if the manna ceased at the first Passover feast after we arrived in what was to become our homeland.

'God's bread is at the heart of life,' taught Jesus, 'It belongs to eternity, and fills all who eat with a richness of life that is indeed part of eternity. And eternity is not some distant or otherworldly idea - it is about our lives and the way we live them on earth, here and now.'

He described it in such a way that his hearers were carried along into the possibilities of fuller, deeper and more satisfying life, which was at the heart of Jesus' message constantly. So exciting did he make it that someone called out from the middle of the gathering, 'Master, don't just talk about it. Give us this bread now!'

A titter ran round at this. Exciting as Jesus' preaching was, most people still believed it was rhetorical rather than practical. After all, that was the nature of sermons. But Jesus stopped dead, scanning the congregation for his interlocutor. He found him and looked straight at him. The titter died and there was silence again.

'I am!' said Jesus, 'I am this bread of God. I am he who can open you to the fullness of the joy of life. Come to me and you will need no other sustenance. Open yourself to me and I can satisfy your highest desires. Are you not thirsty for God? Come to me.'

He went on to explain the openness of this invitation, and that it was both for this life and for any future life. This second part, a future life, was something Jesus only mentioned rarely, and partly to help his listeners fit his message into their own framework. Jesus' prime concern was for the quality of life that we share here and now. When he wanted to talk about the fullest possible life he used words like 'eternal' and 'eternity', which in our language are nothing to do with length of time, but to do with depth and quality. They are to do with the unseen world; the *real* world that is the world of God and is hidden within the changes and chances of the world we see. The whole created order is, in a sense, the dress of the world of eternity.

His hearers had been carried along with him before, but now things began to change. Jesus had lifted the challenge up a notch. In particular, after pointing out that not Moses, but God had given the first heavenly bread, he was claiming a higher authority than Moses' in terms of his own bread of eternity. He was, in effect, not only claiming to be the messianic prophet that Moses had promised, but greater than that. People began to mutter, and there was a murmuring throughout the congregation that was very reminiscent of our first reading, where eight times it talks of the people 'muttering' against Moses and against God.

The muttering was taking the form of questioning his credentials. One strand of messianic hope suggested that the Messiah should come from Bethlehem in Judæa, and another, that the Messiah would be direct from God, or heaven, interpreted in a rather literal way. Jesus fitted neither of these, thought the congregation.

'We know Joseph, his father,' said those from Nazareth.

'And his mother,' others added.

'He's a Galilean; a good place, but hardly Heaven,' quipped someone.

Jesus, of course, did not view things in this literal way; for him heaven was almost a synonym for his 'world of eternity'.

He decided to continue his sermon.

'Mutter! Mutter!' He chided them. 'You will none of you understand unless you open yourselves to a new sort of hope.

It's no good running round in old, safe circles. The Messiah is far bigger than the old ideas. Let God touch your hearts.'

And then, as is traditional, he led into the second text, normally chosen by the preacher to illustrate the first, and taken from the second reading. We had heard from the book of Isaiah about the new hope offered to us after our captivity in Babylon, and Jesus quoted the promise there, 'Come...and God will teach you directly.'

'I am that teacher. I do indeed come from God, and know him and what he offers.

'Hear then the word of truth' he continued, his voice lancing through the synagogue and out to the throng beyond in the late afternoon sunshine. 'If you enter into what I offer you, you will live the true full life. I am. I am God's bread of eternity. Our ancestors ate Moses' bread, and they died. It was only a shadow of what God now offers you in me. Come, eat, and enter into a life that is not bound by time and death. I am God's bread. It is for all the world. My body I give as God's bread to you.'

If the crowd had muttered before, they were arguing now. Jesus had racked up his divisive challenge yet another notch. He was determined not to make it too easy for them and thus lead to the mistakes of the day before on the hillside. The synagogue authorities were arguing too, even the steward of the day, whose duty it was to keep order. He, poor man, had quite lost the situation by now.

'What's this about eating his body?' they were saying.

The more literalistic were almost spluttering phrases such as, 'No better than cannibals,' and even the more profound were looking very shocked at Jesus' violent image of God's teaching as human flesh. God's teaching as food they had heard of before, but to make it this personal and offensive!

Now was the time for Jesus to pacify them, I thought, and glancing at the others, I could see they thought the same. This could land us in even deeper trouble than yesterday. But no. Jesus was ready with yet another twist of the screw.

'Hear then the word of truth,' he called across the hubbub, and raising his voice even higher, announced his concluding remarks in prophetic tones.

'Eat my body. Drink my blood, or you cannot live as God intended you. Eat my body, that is food indeed. Drink my blood and get high on life itself. You will become one with me, and I will live in you. You will be as close to God as I am myself. Indeed, God sent me just for this.'

He then quoted his text again, contrasting the bread of the wilderness with the bread of the psalmist, and in a way that unmistakably challenged everybody present. He stood up, to indicate that the sermon was over.

There was chaos in the synagogue. I suppose the steward pronounced a blessing and dismissal, but if he did, no-one took a blind bit of notice. All were having to grapple with the challenge of Jesus. There was no easy Messianism today; no chance of a mistake. Jesus had delivered his message directly and in terms of biblical images with which they were all familiar.

The Friday-afternoon sermon is supposed to send us off to the Friday-evening Sabbath meal, which in even the poorest of families is as near as possible to a feast, in order to honour God. Not one person who heard that sermon would be able to sit down to supper without Jesus' words ringing in their ears. How many would begin to understand was another matter. Jesus had managed to shock nearly everybody. I suddenly heard in my mind the words he had addressed to Andrew, Peter and myself shortly after we met him: 'I don't want an army.' There was no chance of that now; he'd be lucky to be left with a company!

We had arranged to share our own Sabbath meal about a mile and a half down the coast on a stretch of shoreline which we knew and loved, and where plentiful fresh water sprang from the hillocks that bordered the lake and ran across the beach into the sea. Given our increasing numbers, we had taken to sharing this key meal of the week *al fresco*, and, in fine weather, camping where we ate so that we could wake and spend the day together in the games and relaxation that mark the special nature of our Sabbath, and make it such a treasured possession of our religion.

Some of us went in the boats, and others walked; it made very little difference in terms of time.

When we got there, it seemed as if our numbers were considerably down, and indeed there were quite a few sullen and unhappy faces among the disciples who had turned up. Jesus had been very quiet in the boat, and he stepped ashore last. He then simply walked away, ungallantly leaving Mary, who had been holding the prow, to manage on her own.

He faced his group of disparate followers and said, 'You're offended at what I said.'

'It's too literal - too real and hard,' said one, reluctantly.

'No-one can believe in what you've just preached,' added another.

Jesus looked piercingly at them. Was he going to antagonise even them?

'Too real and hard?' he demanded. 'What if you were in truth to see heaven and earth, time and eternity united in me?'

'It's not that you are not close to God,' said one, 'That we can believe. It's the eating of your flesh. It has scandalised everybody.'

'Oh you literalists!' exclaimed Jesus. 'Flesh is irrelevant. Life and eternity are things of the Spirit. In truth, you don't see this, do you?'

He took some of the bread that was laid on a rock ready for the Sabbath feast, tore it in two, and said, 'Eat this, this is my flesh; bread from heaven.'

He took a flagon, unstoppered it, and poured out some wine into a beaker, saying as he did so, 'Look, here is my blood poured out for you.'

Whether he meant them to share at that moment, I do not

know, although after that time he often did this for us, giving thanks and breaking bread, and sharing with us at a special meal. Indeed, we have always done it ourselves since. It was, however, more than the doubters could take. They looked at one another, then across at Jesus, standing there a few yards up the beach, with Mary still hanging onto the boat in the background. The setting sun was on his face and in his hair, and there was the flash of challenge in his eyes.

By far the most of his disciples turned, in ones and twos and then more numerously, and walked up the beach to the lakeside road, away from the one whose challenge was too great.

There was a deep silence among the few who remained, broken by Andrew's sandals scuffing across the pebbles of the beach. He had just noticed Mary's predicament, and went to help her with the boat. Then Nathaniel moved, and in a way curiously reminiscent of the gathering of the fragments on the previous day, he picked up the broken halves of Jesus' loaf, where he had laid them on the rock before tackling the wine.

Jesus looked around. 'What of you few? Will you leave too?'

I had a vision of everyone deserting him except for myself. I couldn't, of course; it would have emptied my life of all that I had won over the last year. I had a picture of myself and Andrew back to square one with Jesus, for I realised that he too would never go. And then I realised that Nathaniel would never...nor Mary...and never our Rock.

On cue to my thought, Peter spoke.

'Leave?' he said, 'Whatever for? Where else can we go to explore your "eternity"?'

And then, rare for Peter, a flash of pure theology.

'We know you. We have come to recognise you. You're God's chosen one.' He spoke for us all.

'Chosen?' Jesus replied, 'I chose you, and look at the results.' His eyes swept the almost deserted beach, and came back to rest on the few of us remaining.

'And not all of you will remain true.'

Fourth Witness

But Peter had done and said what was necessary. His loyalty, our Rock, had crystallised how we all felt, the small remainder. His words had focused what we really believed, and enabled us to make an important transition. This was from the first year, when we had been an easy-going and popular movement, into a new and much more scary life-style. The second, and final, year was as a group increasingly shunned and under suspicion, especially by the authorities. These two days marked the turning point, and Peter's words helped us to cross over into our new and more dangerous world.

Chapter 5

After his prediction in the Upper Room of Peter's betrayal - and you can now see why it came as such a shock - Jesus changed tack. Indeed, he seemed now to have said what was burdening him and causing the trouble in his eyes and trembling in his limbs. What came next was much more comforting, although still very puzzling.

Jesus took up the theme of his going away, and our following later. You will remember that we had left Peter wanting to go with Jesus, and not understanding this at all. Not that any of us did, of course.

'Don't look so forlorn! There is no reason to be so fearful. God's heart is large, and there is room for you all. I leave you now to go and open the way for you into the heart of God. I lead the way, and then I shall return to you. Then we shall be at one together in the life of eternity. So now you understand where I am going, and you too know the road.'

There were one or two dubious nods at this. It sounded plausible, but also a bit too yonderly.

Thomas cut through all this with the blunt question that was lurking in all of us.

'Master, we don't understand where on earth you are going; so we haven't the faintest idea of a road.'

A murmur of agreement ran round the room, and I saw Martha nodding her vigorous assent.

'I am,' (that name again) said Jesus, 'I am the road. I lead to the true life of fullness and depth. I am the road into the heart of God. You know me well, now, but when you really come to know me you will know and see God.'

Martha, I saw, had the beginning of understanding dawning in her eyes, and I remembered that recently Jesus had said something very similar to her. More of that in a minute.

There was something dawning in Philip's eyes, too, but he, like most of us, was still a long way from understanding. Jesus was shooting out these ideas and pictures at us, and it was happening fast. If you think we were slow on the uptake, you must remember we were *hearing* these things, and some for the first time. We were not, like you, sitting and reading at leisure. Indeed, leisure would be the last word to describe the atmosphere of the room in which Jesus had more or less said he would be dead by this time tomorrow, and hinted at the most ugly and degrading death of all.

Philip tried desperately to keep up.

'Master, if you show us God, so that we *can* see him, then perhaps it will all be clear to us.'

The idea of *seeing* God, is, as all Jews know, ludicrous. It is another of the things that separates us from most other religions with their statues and pictures of gods. Jesus had talked about seeing God before, and made it very clear that this was seeing with the inward eye, with the heart, if you like. There was just a touch of impatience in his voice as he replied to Philip.

'How long has it been Philip, since we met in Cana? Do you still not know who I am? I am the nearest you can come to 'seeing' God. What I teach you is God's. I live in God and he lives in me.'

By now we knew what he meant by 'life' and 'living' - this was the whole purpose of the religious life - to engage with the whole rainbow of the world, and not just the surface world of black and white. What was harder was to understand how this happened by sticking close to Jesus, especially a Jesus who was 'going away'.

Jesus answered the unasked question.

'Just think back to what life has been like for us, together,' he said, and paused, so that we knew he meant us to do that there and then.

I thought of the challenges and the puzzlements, the excitements and the moments of deep, deep joy. Of the satisfaction that takes one out of space and time when an insight actually works and unlocks one of the enigmas of the world. I thought of those moments of eternity when Jesus was at work with one of his signs.

Exactly chiming with my thoughts, he said, 'At the lowest, trust the feelings that you had when you saw beneath the signs.'

Martha, who out of all of us seemed to have understood this best, was weeping gently, and at the same time smiling through her tears at Jesus. He was smiling back, and nodding. No spoken word passed, but suddenly I could almost hear the unspoken sharing.

'Yes, I understand. I felt it even before you raised my brother. It was not what you did, nor even the words you said. It was in the closeness when I trusted you, and felt God's love entwine us.'

'Beloved,' I felt the response, and by the use of that name felt myself joined to Martha in her understanding, our understanding of Jesus, 'Beloved, did I not say that even death has no power over us when we share in God?'

Chapter 6

I have mentioned Jesus' signs before, and what you have just read about Martha refers to perhaps his most notorious sign, and certainly the one that led most directly to the events of the final days. It was the last straw as far as the authorities were concerned, and signed Jesus' death warrant.

Having said that, it had been clear for some time that they were going to eliminate him if they could. There had been three attempts to have him arrested, and two attempts to have the mob lynch him, all of which had come to nothing. Judæa, and especially Jerusalem, had become just too dangerous, and we were virtually in hiding across the River Jordan in Peræa.

It was just a few weeks before that final supper that I have been describing to you.

The home of Martha and Mary is in Bethany. (Not the Bethany where John had pointed Jesus out to us and it all began, but the much better known one about three miles from Jerusalem along the Jericho road. Actually it is only two miles if you don't mind climbing and you take the short cut over the Mount of Olives.) They lived there with their brother Lazarus, and Jesus was very fond of the three of them. Their home was always open to us and they never seemed to feel that our mixed band of uncertain and varying number was anything other than a pleasure to entertain.

Lazarus fell ill, and gradually it became clear to the sisters that it was serious. They must have hesitated a long time before they felt so desperate that they had to let Jesus know. They would be very unwilling to put us at risk, which the message did, as of course it raised the question of whether we should venture back into Judæa or not. Lazarus was plainly too ill to know anything about this, or he would have prevented them sending a message, we were sure.

You can imagine the debates among us on hearing of this, but Jesus cut through it all.

'This will not end in death, but in exaltation. Don't worry, but wait and see what you will see.'

The upshot of this was that we stayed where we were for another couple of days.

On the evening of the second day, over dinner, Jesus himself raised the whole business again.

'How about a walk over into Judæa, tomorrow?' he asked. 'I want to go and visit Bethany.' This caused us to react in consternation, and we had good reason.

Only too vivid in our minds was the memory of the hostile group from the authorities hemming him in and demanding that he give them a straight 'yes' or 'no' as to whether he was the Messiah or not. This had been a few months previously at the winter festival of the Dedication of the Temple (which we call Hanukkah), and Jesus had been teaching in Solomon's colonnade, which runs inside the length of the east wall of the Temple forecourt, and so is protected against the cold December winds.

Jesus had been giving the authorities a hard time. He had taken up the various Hanukkah Bible-readings about shepherds, and had been comparing himself (using the provocative 'I am' again) to God's good shepherd in contrast to the rulers who were just in it for the pay and perks, he suggested. He had been particularly hard on the reform party, whom he compared to robbers and brigands who attack the flock.

We had been up to Cæsarea Philippi that summer, in order to get right away after the events I told you about around the Sea of Galilee, and Jesus had been particularly interested in the cave where the pagan shepherd-god Pan was supposed to be born, and in the new temples built there by the first Herod, his son Philip and their Roman friends. Indeed, the pagans call the town 'Paneas', after Pan. Jesus seemed to have this in mind in his stories about shepherds, because he referred to other flocks (i.e. the Gentile pagans) for which he was also responsible.

It was not really surprising that the religious had reacted so violently, and in answer to their demand to know if he were the Messiah, the true shepherd of Israel, he had more or less told them that they didn't belong to God's flock and that not only was he indeed God's shepherd, but more than that - for these purposes he and God were much the same.

This was a claim that fell within the legal definition of blasphemy (making oneself out to be God), for which the penalty can be death by stoning. The leaders picked up stones, and incited the bystanders to join in, and it was only by rapid use of certain texts in the Bible which Jesus could cite in his defence that he was not stoned there and then. If he had been, I doubt we would have escaped, for in law we were certainly implicated in Jesus' claims. He left the scene having rephrased his claim in terms of God living the life of eternity in Jesus and vice versa, but the dormant warrant for his arrest was immediately renewed, and that is why we had come to Peræa.

So you see why we were so concerned when Jesus announced his intention to return to Judæa, and more than that, to go so close to Jerusalem as Bethany. Philip summed it up.

'Teacher, last time we were there we just escaped stoning! There is a warrant out for your arrest. You really want to go back there?'

'It's a matter of timing,' said Jesus. 'God's timing and mine,' and he came out with one of his favourite proverbs, 'There are twelve daylight hours, and twelve dark. The wise walk in the day.' He added, 'Walk in the light of the world.'

He had used this last phrase on a couple of previous

occasions, and was to use it again, referring to himself as the light of the world (using his contentious 'I am'). It was another way of talking about the life of eternity, for which 'light' is a very good picture. People so often seem to live their lives in broken bits, as if they are scratching around in the dark. Full and joyful life, although by its very nature it is spontaneous and full of serendipity, has rather the feeling of being lived by someone at home in a well-lit landscape.

That it was a matter of timing wasn't enough for us, even with the proverb, because we thought his timing was very bad, and that it was just too plain dangerous. So Jesus added another reason.

'Lazarus has fallen asleep;' he said, 'dead to the world.'

'Then he will get better. Surely sleep is the best thing for him?' someone said.

'Not this sleep. This is the sleep of death,' replied Jesus, 'and I must go and wake him. I'm glad we weren't there. It gives an opportunity for you to understand.'

This last remark slipped by us; we were too concerned at the prospect of going back into the danger zone. We were not at our safest here in Peræa, which was part of Herod's territory, and I for one would have been happier to be back up in the Decapolis again, or in Philip's province. It seemed madness to leave even this relative security for somewhere so close to Jerusalem. Thomas had the last word, in that lugubrious way of his.

'We'd all better go. At least we can die with him.' This had all the satisfaction of the 'I told you so' proved right, but it would be wrong to ignore Thomas' very considerable courage here, for I think he truly believed what he said. I certainly more than half-believed him, and even sunny Andrew was looking very serious.

The journey was about 25 miles, and we discussed whether to make an early start and try to do it all in a day, or whether to break the journey half way. Several of us felt it would be a mistake to do the long climb from near Jericho up to Bethany (an ascent of over 3,000 feet) in the afternoon sun. Jesus decided it by saying that he would rather appear earlier in the day at Bethany, and then put some distance between Bethany and wherever we slept.

This was encouraging, as Jesus seemed to be showing signs of discretion, and I said so.

Jesus laughed at me.

'Beloved, the time is right. But it is not yet *that* right time. I will tell you when it is.'

Two days later we arrived near Bethany just before noon. We had left the road at a big bend a couple of miles to the east, and made our way up onto the ridge. It was a shorter and harder way, but it had the advantage of bringing us down into the village by the back lane. Even so, our approach was noticed, and we in turn saw quite a crowd in front of the house. It was clear that the mourning process was in full swing, and had been so for some days.

Martha was quickly told of our arrival. She is the sort of person who is always the first to be made aware of events, and is also often the first to adapt to new situations. She had managed the home, and indeed most of the village, ever since the death of her parents.

She immediately slipped away from the wake, and headed up the path to meet us. She was not sure what Jesus would want to do, since he was, to all intents and purposes, too late, and, of course, it was dangerous for him to be here at all. Her first thought as she accepted Jesus' embrace was a practical one, and it was for our safety.

'Master, I am glad to see you, but this is not safe. There are many here from Jerusalem who have come to share in our grief. I sent a message four days ago saying that my brother had died, and you were not to risk coming.'

'Don't worry, Martha,' Jesus replied, 'all will be well.'

'We really needed you some days ago,' she said. 'I am sure you could have saved Lazarus. You are so close to God. Even now...,' and she bit off the thought, as if it was too silly or dangerous to speak it aloud.

Jesus held her away from him so that he could search her face. Incongruously he was smiling at her, or perhaps at the words she hadn't said.

'Martha, your brother will rise from the dead.'

'Oh, I know,' she replied, not looking directly at him, 'I know that he, and all of us, will rise from the dead at the end of time.'

Something rather like disappointment part-clouded her face, and her brow furrowed slightly. Martha was an excellent theologian, and she and Jesus could often leave the rest of us labouring to keep up, but their talk had never been conventional. She had not expected the trite phrases of consolation from Jesus, and was surprised and a little hurt that all he could offer her was the traditional resurrection hope.

But Jesus had something very different in mind.

'I am!' he said.

'*I* am resurrection. I am now, and the life of eternity is now. This makes death merely a part of things; just an adventure in the wholeness of life. If you live in me, death becomes part of life itself. Death has no power over us when we share in God.'

He paused, and suddenly looked very anxious. The answer to the next question was vitally important. The whole of what was about to happen hung upon it. He wanted, yearned for Martha to see the truth that the sign was about to reveal, but if she could see it first, then she would have come as close as anyone yet to the secrets of God that Jesus sought to share.

'Do you believe me?' he asked her.

Martha looked straight into his eyes. You could almost say that her heart looked straight into his. Jesus was still holding her shoulders, and she reached up to cradle his elbows in her hands.

'Yes. I believe you. God has sent you into the world to unite us with God in you. I know who you are. You are the Messiah.' Then she added in Greek, the international language, as if to make it clear that this was for all the world, Gentiles and Jews, 'You are Christ.'

The moment held. And we, privileged onlookers and sharers in this, held still too. There had been much talk of Jesus as the Messiah, and we all thought that it was the case in some form. We had said it to each other about him, but Martha was the first of us to say it to him. Not even Peter, in his declaration in Galilee, had used the word itself.

Martha had made her statement of faith, and it was definitive. It stood for us all; it stood both in this world and in the life of eternity, and it stood in her name.

Jesus was going to go to Lazarus' tomb, but before that he also wanted a word with Mary, and so Martha went back to let her sister know that Jesus was asking for her.

Mary was seated just inside the doorway of the house, out of the direct sunlight, talking with the many consolers who had come to visit. This visiting is the usual practice with us. It did mean, however, that she was right in the centre of things, and when Martha whispered her message to Mary, there was no way that she could leave without drawing attention to herself. She stood up at once, and stepped out of the doorway into the sunlight, where we could see her from our vantage point on the hillside just above the house. She then set off, not straight towards us, but up the village street, as if making for the cemetery, presumably so that people would think that she was going to visit her brother's tomb.

If that was her intention, the ruse did not work, for several well-meaning people followed her, no doubt to give her support in her grieving. On realising this, Mary changed direction, and came between the houses and out onto the hillside where we were waiting for her.

As she drew near, we could see the brave face that she was

putting on things, and she forced a bright smile when she saw Jesus. She came towards him, and he held out his arms to her. This was just too much for Mary. Her face crumpled, the tears came, and falling at Jesus' feet she hugged his legs. Using almost the same words as Martha, she poured out her thoughts to him.

'Master, how we needed you. If only you had been here, I'm sure you could have saved him.'

This was clearly no time to talk about it; Mary was very different from her sister, and Jesus, knowing this, had always treated them very differently.

'Where is his body?' he asked. There was a catch in his voice, and glancing sharply at him, I realised that he too was weeping. 'Take me to him.'

There were many there anxious to help by showing the way. Death brings out a helplessness in us that makes us keen to render *any* service, however small. They also saw his tears, and I overheard snatches of conversation among the mourners.

'Look, he really loved him!'

'If he'd been here...'

'I know a man blind from birth that he cured, surely...'

'...too late now.'

We arrived at the tomb, and Jesus was clearly very upset. This was less on Lazarus' account than on that of the sisters, but I suspect also it was at the prospect of the awesomeness of what he proposed to do. Not that he had doubts about his ability, he was too close to God for that, it was more that he knew both its significance in terms of the life of eternity, but also how many would interpret it in this-worldly terms.

The family tomb was a cave at the side of the cemetery, and had a stone rolled across the entrance. This was an indication of the standing of Lazarus and his family, as relatively few can afford to be buried in this way. The opening was fairly small, one would have to stoop low to go in, but we knew that it would open out inside and there might well be more than one room with shelves along the walls and grave-spaces side by side going back into the rock.

Jesus said, 'Take away the stone.'

There was a murmur of surprise at this, and Martha, ever practical, pointed out that after four days in our climate this would be very unpleasant. Jesus looked at her.

'Did I not say, "Death has no power over us when we share in God"? Trust me, as I know you do.'

None of the onlookers had moved, so Peter stepped forward, and assisted by his brother and James, strained at the stone until it rolled in its rough groove to the side.

Jesus glanced upwards, and then closed his eyes. Those standing near him heard him say, 'Thank you, God! It is for their sake that we do this.'

And then he took three steps towards the tomb. Almost casually, as if calling to a friend just inside a house, he then spoke.

'Lazarus. Come on out.'

We heard a shuffle from inside the tomb. We saw a flash of white inside the entrance, and then Lazarus, stooping over to get through the low door, and very much impeded by his shroud and headcloth, inched his way out. He straightened up.

'Undo him,' said Jesus, and Andrew unwound the headcloth, so that we could see Lazarus, whole and alive, blinking in the sunlight.

You can imagine how soon *this* story was all over Jerusalem. There were many who saw it, and some of them were of the reform party, and others felt it their duty to inform the authorities. We heard later (as you know, we had friends in high places) that this precipitated a Council meeting chaired by Caiaphas, our High Priest, who was our *de facto* ruler under the

Romans. He decided that things had gone far enough, and must be brought to an end. The earlier decisions to have Jesus arrested were given more force, and it was decided that as soon as they had him, they would arrange an immediate execution.

It may seem strange that Jesus was causing them such concern, but this was because, in a way, the rulers understood him better than most. It was not the wonders that he was doing. Wonder-workers are not all that rare, and even raising people from the dead is quite well-attested. It was the claims that Jesus made for himself that worried our leaders, and the fact that they *did* understand what a sign was (quite different from just a random miracle, however wonderful), and knew that if others did too, they would inevitably draw messianic conclusions about Jesus. They were still living in a mindset that linked 'Messiah' with 'king' and 'king' with 'political power' and 'insurrection', and this was what frightened them so much about Jesus. They had also judged his claims about God, by far the most important thing to them as to us, and had decided they were false.

We heard that Caiaphas had said that it was right for one man to die for the people, and in a curious way he spoke truer than he knew, and for not just the Jewish people, but for everybody. But then, he *was* the High Priest, and God spoke through him whether he, Caiaphas, realised it or not.

We left that same day, not even staying overnight, and made our way to Ephraim. This is a fair way to the north of Jerusalem, and close to the edge of the wilderness, should we have a need to disappear from view.

Chapter 7

The raising of Lazarus was the event that notched the authorities up into a final determination to finish Jesus off, and his pretensions with him.

Although we had taken refuge in Ephraim, Jesus had been determined to go to Jerusalem for this Passover, and made it clear to us that somehow it would be the decisive moment in his struggle with the authorities. He referred to it as 'his time'.

We stayed overnight at Bethany, and this was the occasion when Mary took the ointment and washed Jesus' feet with it - the action that had caused Judas such annoyance. He had felt that it was a terrific waste of a very expensive ointment, and talked grandly of giving all the money we could have raised on it to the poor. To be honest, I suspect Judas was much more concerned about the waste of money than about the poor. He was our treasurer, and could get very money-minded, even greedy about it. Jesus had told him in no uncertain terms that Mary had done the right thing, and indeed had prepared Jesus' body for burial. He was talking about his death more and more, and it made us very uneasy.

When we arrived at the city itself the crowds were there ahead of us, camping out to the north and west of Jerusalem, as was usual at this time, when so many wanted to be there. They got wind of our coming, and insisted on greeting Jesus as if he were a king making a triumphal entry into his capital. Jesus had defused this, to some extent, by treating the whole thing as a joke, and even going to the lengths of borrowing a donkey to ride into Jerusalem - hardly a kingly steed! Later, I remembered how one of our prophets had suggested that this was the way the Messiah would come, and uneasily I wondered how many others in Jerusalem, especially among our enemies, were mulling over the same passage.

This had been on the Tuesday, and it was now Thursday evening when we were eating together in the Upper Room, and when Jesus was continuing his teaching to us after the foot-washing.

It became clearer and clearer that this was a 'good bye' and he was concerned to say all that needed to be said. This is why I need to keep referring back to earlier episodes, because they all contained the seeds of his message and pointed to this last great sharing of his teaching with us.

There was a new element too. He was giving us instructions for a new life when he would not be with us in the same way, and he was preparing us so that we would not be caught on the hop. Not that he had a great deal of success here; we were still totally unprepared for what happened, and were only able to understand it in retrospect. However, this was hardly Jesus' fault.

One of the (many) highlights of that evening was a picture he painted for us of a vine tree. He asked us to imagine that he was a vine tree and that we were the branches. He wriggled his legs forward and swung round so that he was sitting on the couch, and stretched his arms out in a very tree-like manner. He began with another of his 'I am' lines.

'Look at me,' he said. 'I am a vine tree. You're the branches. God's the gardener. Now God loves wine, and he wants a good crop of grapes.'

He reached out to the table and took a bunch of grapes and dangled them from his hand to illustrate his story.

'How does he get such good grapes?' he asked. 'He prunes the tree, and cleans it up. This has to be really drastic. A well-pruned tree looks just like a dead stump.'

He pulled his arms into his lap and hunched over.

'It looks dead, but the new life then comes.' He grew his

branches again as he spoke. 'This is how it is with you and me. But the branches that have been cut off, they are dead, and the best use for them is as fuel. Vine-wood makes a lovely bonfire. You are not those branches, but the ones that have been pruned to give new grapes. It hurts, and what is coming to us all will hurt, but if you stay with me, you will grow good grapes.'

He was now sitting with his arms stretched wide, as if to embrace us all, and, indeed the whole world beyond us.

'Live in me, just like the vine-branches live in the vine. The vine *is* its branches, really. Love as I love, and I will be in you, just as God will be. Love is what makes us one. Love will make grapes, and grapes will make wine, and wine is a sign of our joy, the joy of living in eternity.'

Wine was important to Jesus. It symbolised joy, but he also used it as an image for the outpouring of love. He linked it to the bread that he shared when he sometimes gave them to us at a meal as a way of thinking of the unity we have with him and with God in the full life.

He had also begun his ministry in Galilee with wine.

Chapter 8

I have told you about Jesus' last public sign, and I should tell you about his first, the one that was to set the tone for his Northern ministry, and which, in a way, underlay the whole of his teaching.

This takes us back to the much happier days near the start of our time together, long before we were thinking ahead to where it was all going, and before the opposition built up, especially in Jerusalem. Galilee, even given the events surrounding the sermon in Capernaum that I told you about, was always a much happier place for us.

You may remember that a few days after we had first met Jesus, we travelled north with him to Cana. He had been invited to a family wedding, and it was while we were waiting for the wedding to begin that Philip had joined us, and introduced Nathaniel into our group. Well, the story I have to tell you now concerns that same wedding.

Our weddings go on for some days, and this one was no exception. It was a lovely spring that year, and Cana, on its tel, faces south across the valley, and is something of a suntrap. In idyllic weather, warm, but with enough of a breeze to keep us cool and fresh, we feasted and rejoiced with the young couple, and took our ease on the top of the hill just to the south of the village, where everything had been set out.

There were the usual three couches at the centre of things, and on the top couch reclined the bride and groom, either side of the chosen host, an elder of Cana, who was an old and valued friend of both families. To the left and right were the proud parents, and others would come and go from the remaining places. Around them and stretching down from them were other couches and chairs, and the tables bearing food and drink from which we guests were expected to help ourselves. Any friends of the family automatically became guests, and so we were made heartily welcome as belonging to Jesus. 'The more the better' is the view of any parent at their child's wedding.

Jesus' mother had had a hand in the preparations, and, along with several other women, all related in different ways to the couple, kept an eye on how things were going in general, and on the catering in particular. It was with regard to the catering that Jesus was led to display his first sign.

Cana is not very big, and by the third day it transpired that we had more or less drunk the place dry. Not only had all the wine bought for the wedding been used up, but also all the extra in the village given or sold to the anxious organisers when they realised they had miscalculated.

Jesus' mother, being a helper, was deeply involved in this, and was very concerned that something be done. A wedding that ran out of wine would be a permanent embarrassment to all concerned, and the couple could look forward to a lifetime of comments beginning, 'Wasn't it at your wedding...' Not having any other idea, his mother came across to where Jesus was lying on the ground, propped up on one elbow and engaged in a fascinating, if somewhat desultory, conversation with the five of us.

'Son, they are about to run out of wine. There's nothing left but what you see on the tables.'

Jesus was never one to bother with provisions or their procurement, and his response was less than helpful.

'Not my line. You're the woman, here. What d'you expect me to do about it?'

This was typical 'son talk', of course, and the response was typical 'mother'. She took no offence at all, smiled indulgently at her first-born, and said, 'In your own good time.' She then turned to go back to the tables, but with a parting shot over her shoulder.

'In case it *does* turn out to be time you did something, I'll tell the servants to follow your instructions.'

With this, and with what was almost a cheeky grin, she left us.

We went back to our conversation, but Jesus did not join in, and had gone quiet, clearly dwelling on the brief exchange. Nathaniel was flying one of his wilder theological kites, mainly to see what reaction he'd get, when Jesus, who wasn't listening to a word, cut right across him. Jesus had obviously regarded the party as time off, and wasn't keen to return to work, so to speak.

'Bother Mother. She's quite right of course,' he muttered, and then said more loudly to us, but still in an undervoice, 'Stay still now, and watch, and *please* don't get the wrong end of the stick.'

He rolled up onto his knees and then stood up and stretched. He paused, surveying the wedding scene. Then he walked across to the servants by one of the wine tables, and began talking to them. He was clearly asking about the wine situation. It then seemed that he was asking about containers, for they showed him various wineskins, which with a wave of his hand he rejected.

Behind them, in the shadow of the low building that capped one of Cana's many water cisterns, there were half a dozen of the large stone water jars that are used for ritual water. I should explain that we use water a great deal for the ritual cleansing of ourselves, our bedding and furniture, and especially our eating and cooking utensils. Stone is supposed to be particularly resistant to impurity, and you will see these jars everywhere. The ones by the cistern were rather larger than average, ranging from twenty to thirty gallons, but by no means as big as some you may see.

Jesus was gesturing towards them, probably asking if they had yet been filled, or if they were the 'empties', and then the servants went over to them. They didn't seem too pleased with whatever Jesus had said to them, and immediately I could see why. With Jesus standing over them, they were painstakingly drawing water bucket by bucket from the cistern and filling the jars. Jesus kept them at it until all six were completely full.

This took several minutes. While they were doing this, Jesus walked back to the table, picked up a dipper and a flagon, and returned to the jars. He then dipped in one of the jars, filled the flagon, had a little taste from the dipper, and sent one of the boys off to the host.

The servants were looking anywhere but at the top table. They obviously thought that a well-oiled guest was playing an elaborate practical joke. We, on the other hand, couldn't tear our eyes away, and I noticed Jesus' mother, with a wry and amused half-smile on her lips, moving to a position just behind the top couch.

Contents from the flagon splashed into the expensive crystal goblet that was passed around Cana for weddings, and the host raised it to his lips for the usual tasting. He would, of course, say the polite thing, whatever the wine was like. Then a curious expression crossed his face, and he drank again, more deeply. Then he called across to the bride's parents, in voice that everyone at the wedding could hear.

'But this is vintage! As fine a wine as ever I've tasted! Fancy keeping this back until now!'

The servants looked thunderstruck, but they didn't have time to speculate, because there was an immediate rush on the wine. Everyone wanted to check out the host's verdict for themselves. They were kept even busier than Jesus had kept them until the top-table guests were replenished, and flagons filled and re-filled on the side tables.

In any case, the most that they had seen was a miracle. We had seen something else. We had seen a sign.

It was the first, and we didn't yet understand Jesus' special use of that word, but we *did* understand that we had seen something that no-one else present had seen. We had seen the closeness between Jesus and God acted out before our eyes. If you like, a veil had been lifted, and we saw Jesus in a new light. It was the same Jesus, and it was a matter of confirming something that we had already been reaching out towards. But it was special.

As I say, it was the first sign, and it set the tone. Partly it was the sheer prodigality of making all that wine; far more than we actually needed, and *that* was about the prodigality of love. God's prodigality and love first, but ours also. Partly it was the joy of the moment, both the joy engendered in the couple happy and the feast saved, but also our own joy as witnesses to it. But as much as anything it was about richness, as if all our religious insight was as weak as water, compared with what was going to happen to us now, with Jesus here.

It was followed later by another sign, very different in character, and this time in Jerusalem.

If the wine at the wedding set the tone for Jesus' work in Galilee, and in general for all those who are open to the wider possibilities of life, then in Jerusalem his first open act set a different and more sombre tone. It set the mood for confrontation with the authorities, for opposition by those who did not accept either Jesus or his claims, and in general for all who reject what Jesus offers.

It was shortly before our first Passover with Jesus, not long after we had met him and gone to Cana with him, and two years before the last and fatal Passover upon which our story centres.

Jesus had gone with his family to stay in Capernaum for a few days, and we had left him there and gone on ahead up to Jerusalem, having arranged to meet there before the feast. My family home is in Jerusalem, and I wanted to spend a few days there.

The week before the Passover is spent in matters of ritual

purification. The ordinary business of life renders it almost impossible not to come into contact with various forms of uncleanness, and as it is important to eat the Passover in a state of ritual purity, most of us come early to Jerusalem, and spend some time in preparation. Jesus worried less about these things than most; he had his own views on what makes a person clean, which were much more to do with living the full life in contact with God.

As the time came when we had agreed to meet, we were at the Temple before Jesus. We were waiting for him in the outer fore-court, the main concourse of the Temple, known to many as 'the court of the Gentiles'. Everybody except certain Temple officials has to enter from the south, up the great tunnel-ramp that is part of the first Herod's massive reconstruction. Just beyond the top of the ramp is a good rendezvous, as it is difficult to miss one another there.

By the same token, it is the best place for the traders. Most of us bring our own birds and animals for sacrifice, and especially at the Passover, and they are then inspected by the proper authorities to ensure that they are unflawed. This can take time, and some people prefer to buy ready-inspected animals, which are sold in the Temple precincts themselves. These are, needless to say, considerably more expensive. There are also money-changers there, because we are not allowed to bring pagan money, often stamped with the images of kings or gods, into the Temple itself. The only legal tender within the Temple is the shekel, which is free of offending images. The money-changers, too, make quite a profit.

As we were waiting for Jesus, and gazing at the latest building work (the Temple was still under construction, although more-or-less finished), we heard a commotion around the stalls. Together with everyone else, we made our way over to see what was going on. The traders were themselves an unruly lot, and there were often disputes arising from the bartering, and not infrequently these degenerated into fights.

To our surprise, indeed horror, we discovered Jesus in the thick of some affray. It was very clear, however, that he was not the victim. Quite the reverse. He had the whip hand; literally, as he was wielding a knotted rope, with which he was chastising any trader unwary enough to get within reach. He had upended some of the tables, and, to the delight of the urchins, there were coins rolling everywhere. There was chaos among the animals, too, and bird-cages overturned and gaping, whilst their erstwhile prisoners escaped into the air.

Jesus had created a large circle around himself, and it was clear that no-one dared approach him. He was breathing heavily after his exertions, and between breaths he called in a prophetic voice to the astonished crowd.

'Remove these things. This is a place of prayer, not trade. If you are here for purity, purify your motives.'

He was clearly angry, and something had touched him on the raw, maybe an attempt to cheat someone who was vulnerable, or maybe too much avarice in someone's dealings.

The Temple police had reacted quickly, and wisely. Rather than sailing in and provoking a riot - for the traders were not popular, and not a few of the public would have gone to Jesus' aid - they fetched some members of the Council. It was a religious matter, and the Elders were the experts. They decided to try Jesus there and then, according to our custom, and so asked him for his credentials. Some of them, at least those of the reform party, would have had some sympathy with him anyway. They didn't like the traders either. It was a different matter for the priests; they got a share of the profits.

'What is your authority for this?' they began. 'Can you show us a sign that God has called you to this act?'

Jesus simply swept a look around him. He seemed to think that what he had done in itself constituted sufficient sign.

'Well?' they demanded.

'How long has this Temple been under construction?' he asked.

There was a minor dispute over this, but they settled for 'Forty-six years.'

Jesus looked around again, much more slowly now. His interlocutors clearly thought this was a matter of the honour of the Temple, and what was fitting within its walls. Jesus was more concerned with the much deeper matters that the Temple represented, and in particular with the closeness of God. His reply came slowly and clearly.

'Forty-six years? To give people access to God? If it were not here, I could do better in three days!'

No-one knew what he meant by that, and he did not explain himself either to the people, or to us. It became clear in the fullness of time, as it will to you.

The answer, however, was not one that the authorities could deal with, and their first concern was to quieten things down, so they decided to let it pass. Jesus was beginning to acquire a reputation for himself as an able and thoughtful preacher, and people were beginning to take notice. The authorities did not yet know what to make of him, and in any case were probably divided among themselves over the traders.

It did, however, set the tone of confrontation, which was increasingly to be Jesus' lot in Jerusalem.

I am not at all sure that Jesus liked Jerusalem, or indeed any large town or city. It was noticeable that in Galilee he avoided the larger centres of Tiberias and Sepphoris, preferring the smaller lakeside towns or better still camping out in the country. He was a countryman at heart, and went to the big city from a sense of duty, rather than by choice.

Chapter 9

The confrontations with the authorities became the hall-mark of Jesus' work in Jerusalem. They were very much in his mind in the Upper Room, as he moved on from the image of the vine to explain part of what was implied by 'pruning', which he had said would hurt.

Talk of the vine-tree and its fruit had naturally led us to recharge our beakers, and Jesus, reclining again on the couch next to me, said the usual blessing.

'Blessed are you, Lord God of the universe, creator of the fruit of the vine, who gives wine to gladden our hearts.'

He then raised his beaker to us all.

'Blessed are you if you do indeed live in me,' and he drank to us.

'Do you remember what I said a short while ago, after I had washed your feet? Neither menial, nor greater? Well, if servant and master are one, do not expect to escape your master's fate.

'You know how the authorities have treated me. Expect nothing different from those in power, wherever you meet them.

'Powerful people depend on the *status quo*, and we want to change that. We want an end to power that depends on force and fear and manipulation. We prefer the gentle power of love. Those in power have hated me and brought me to this point. They will do as much and more to you.

'You will find yourselves hated because you are a threat. You will be expelled by the religious and killed by the "righteous".

'Power is the way of the world. I don't mean just kings and priests and civil servants. I mean anyone who has carved out a little empire, whether it lies in their home, or at their place of work, or in the knowledge that they think they possess, or in the way they talk to their neighbours as they sit outside of an evening. We threaten them, and must expect their fear and hatred.

'If we teach love, you might say that their hatred is without cause, as we must never use the weapons of the world against the ways of the world. But those who think in the ways of the world can never see that.'

He smiled at us, a smile of wisdom and compassion.

I realised, close to him there on the couch that he was preaching to himself as much as to us. He had a choice; a real one. Even now he could take the path of the world. By power, or by political skill, or even by simple flight, Jesus could easily outflank his enemies if he chose. But that would be to use the ways of the world, and not to take the path of love.

'Don't look so sad,' he went on. 'It is not as black as all that. In fact it is not black at all.

'First, there are many, many people who will hear and accept our message. Deep in their hearts they know that our way is of God, and they yearn to trust it. They want to live lives open to love. They want to embrace not the badness of the world, but the beauty of the world. They will take you to their hearts, and their love renders the scorn of the powerful curiously unimportant.

'Second, I'm not leaving you friendless. I shall return, and you will have a new ally that I shall leave with you. More of that in a minute.

'Third, rejoice! I am about to overcome the ways of the world. Those on the dark side think that it is their time. But now is in fact my time. It is here.'

With that he lay back on the couch. Now Judas was gone there was room for him to stretch as if he was taking his ease after a gruelling race or after a wrestling match. He basked for a moment, as if in the light of God, and then eased himself back onto his elbow, and stretched for his beaker, from which he drank, slow and deep.

This last, both words and gesture, seemed closely linked to what Jesus had been saying earlier about his coming humiliation, and how it would in fact be exaltation. We tried desperately to follow his train of thought, but the ideas were just too paradoxical for us, and, as I said earlier, you must remember that they were being fired at us with extreme rapidity. We had no leisure to cogitate.

That those in power would hate us came as no surprise. Rather, I was surprised that Jesus thought we would escape being brought down with him. I glanced across at Thomas, and heard again in my head his comment 'At least we can die with him', and weighed that with Peter's 'You know I would willingly die for you', so comprehensively contradicted by Jesus. Jesus sensed my thought and turned to me.

'Beloved, you few have been given me by God, and I have no intention of losing any of you. The loss of Judas is more than enough. I am a better shepherd than that.'

Chapter 10

It is time to recount Jesus' stormy relationship with the people at the top.

Really, this had begun with his actions in the Temple, at that first of our three Passovers together, but it came out into the open later in the year, during another of our major feasts, when we went again to Jerusalem.

It started on the Saturday of the feast, when Jesus went to have a look at the Pool of Bethesda and the associated water system. I have told you about his incurable sightseeing, and here he was interested in the various ways water had been brought to the city and stored. The Temple needs a lot of water for washing down during and between sacrifices, and it was supplied by a complex system that had been modified from generation to generation.

There is a new pool just to the north of the Temple, built by the first Herod, which he rather grandly called 'the Pool of Israel', but a few hundred yards further north are two earlier pools. The larger of these is the Sheep Pool (named after the nearby gate through which the sheep for sacrifice are brought) and next to this, separated by a portico is the smaller Pool of Bethesda. This extra portico, in addition to the usual four surrounding the pools, means there are five in all - an unusual feature. The pool complex has been associated with healing for some time, and there was even a pagan sanctuary to the healing god Asklepios at one time, during our period of subjection to the empire left by Alexander the Great.

Jesus was fascinated by all of this. He also noticed a small cluster of people suffering from various ailments clustered around the northern pool, and went to talk with them. It seemed that the association with healing was still very much alive, for they were there waiting for a cure. Apparently, they believed that an angel stirred up the water from time to time, and the first one into the pool at this moment would be healed. After rain it is certainly the case that water bubbles into the pool through the old conduits built by the High Priest Simon about two hundred years ago.

Jesus was talking to a crippled man lying on a pallet.

'How long have you been coming here?' he asked.

'Nigh on thirty-eight years,' the man answered, clearly hoping that Jesus would be a soft touch, as the man lived by begging, and visitors to the major feasts have a duty to give part of what is called the 'second tithe' to the poor.

'Thirty-eight years,' echoed Jesus, 'and not healed? Don't you want to be whole?'

'I don't have a chance, Sir,' said the beggar. 'As you see, I'm lame in both legs, and there is no-one to put me into the pool at the right time. When I start to crawl down the steps, someone else always beats me to it.'

Jesus stretched out his hand to him. The beggar could see it was empty, which didn't please him, but he took hold, nevertheless.

'Be healed and walk!' said Jesus, and hauled him to his feet.

The man was so surprised that he did as Jesus said. His legs regained their natural strength, and he tottered for a moment and then took a couple of steps.

'Take up your bed and go,' said Jesus.

It was a single healing incident, not all that unusual, and Jesus was by no means the only person with healing abilities, but it led to a major confrontation later in the day with the authorities.

The reason for this was because it was Saturday, our Sabbath. The Sabbath is very special to us, and we guard it jealously as a time of rest and enjoyment. It echoes the story of creation, when it is told that God worked for six days, and then took a seventh simply to be and to enjoy his handiwork. Work is forbidden on this day, primarily to protect the vulnerable. It ensures that those who in other societies work without rest (women and slaves spring to mind) are given a day off. More recently some of our reformers have been adding all sorts of rules about what one can and cannot do on the Sabbath, which tends to make it burdensome, rather than a thing of joy.

One of these rules specifically relates to carrying a pallet-bed, and the healed man was stopped and challenged. It transpired that he then promptly blamed Jesus for the whole thing. One wonders whether he wanted healing at all.

Jesus had met him in the Temple later on, and suggested that he open himself to the possibilities of a newer and fuller life rather than moping by a pool all day, and the man had taken the opportunity to ask Jesus' name. He then went and informed on Jesus to the authorities. They in turn hurried down to the Temple to confront Jesus and put him on trial.

He was accused by two of them of Sabbath-breaking, or at least of incitement to Sabbath-breaking; they never made clear whether they regarded the healing itself as work. Jesus however did.

'God may rest and enjoy his world, today,' Jesus replied to the accusation, 'but still is working, sustaining and loving his creation. I have performed exactly this sort of act.'

It was when he said this that the penny dropped, and I realised that we had not witnessed a casual healing, but a sign. His words made things worse, because it sounded as if Jesus was claiming equality with God. He was.

'Hear then the word of truth,' he continued. 'God shares all that he does with me, as his son. I see and know his work, and I work in the same way. I do this so that you may see the wonder and love of God, and so open yourselves to him.'

His accusers felt that Jesus was making their case for them, but our law does not permit anyone to incriminate himself unless it is a deliberate, thought out, and repeated confession.

So they challenged him further, because what he said was getting very close to the technical crime of blasphemy. Jesus continued.

'I may be on trial, but be careful how you judge. God is about life; new life and fuller life. It is my commission from God to share that with you. I come to open to you the life of eternity.'

The warning here reminded his hearers that they must prove their case, otherwise the very fact that they had brought it would mean that they themselves would become the accused, with Jesus as the accuser. This is an important aspect of our legal system, and ensures that people don't bring accusations lightly.

'God does not accuse,' Jesus continued. 'He has given such judgment into the hands of his son, and I have come not as a judge to condemn, but as one who seeks to save. But if I do have to judge, you will have brought it on yourselves, by your own choice.'

This gave his opponents pause. Jesus was quite right as regards his legal point. If they could not prove their case, and blasphemy is notoriously difficult to prove, then they would be on trial themselves. More important still, Jesus was raising the question of choice.

He always saw life in terms of choice. People could choose to open themselves to him, and hence to the life of eternity, or they could turn their backs on it. Once the choice had been presented, there was no evading it, for even to do nothing was to choose. And choice is something upon which we exercise our judgment. Bringing Jesus to judgment meant making the choice. And choice, of course, is habit-forming. The more we choose along a certain line, the more that becomes a part of ourselves. This makes it all the harder to break free, and all the more vital that we do, if our past choices have been destructive to our true self.

Then there was the question, a very real question for them; what if his claims were true? He certainly didn't behave as the traditional kingly Messiah, but then there were so many messianic theories. Jesus had overtones of the Essene's teacher of righteousness, and his cleansing of the Temple could fit into that. Judgment was a part of some messianic ideas, and there was a picture in the book of Daniel that fitted well with what Jesus had just said. So they tried a new tack.

'You are simply making assertions. Have you any witnesses to call?'

Strictly, Jesus only needed witnesses when he moved over to become the prosecution, on the failure of their case, but Jesus was willing to go along with this.

'Yes. You may well not believe me when I say I come from God, but I have three witnesses.

'My first witness is John the Baptist. You know he witnessed to me. He was the lamp to my light, and you enjoyed his glow. He was not the light of God, but a witness to the light. You heard him and cannot deny the truth of what I say.

'My second witness is the work I do. You know that the one God sends will do the works of God. Ask yourselves what has come among you.'

This point came home to the authorities. As I have indicated earlier, they shared Jesus' view on what constituted a sign, and well understood that Jesus was not a miracle-worker in the usual sense, but that his deeds (miraculous or otherwise) were reflections of the theology that he proclaimed. Jesus here was really saying that what he did and what he said formed a coherent and logical whole. If this was the case, even the more traditional leaders would have to think carefully before rejecting him.

Then Jesus came up with a clincher, which left the field to him, that day.

'My third witness is Moses.'

It is assumed that Moses was responsible for most of the

first five books of the Bible, the most important part of it, and which we call 'the Law'. We also call these books 'the books of Moses'. In other words, Jesus was appealing to scripture.

'You are forever consulting the Bible, thinking it will help you live your lives. It will indeed, it will help you embrace the full life, the life of eternity,' he told them. 'Search it, and you will find it points to me.

'It is not a book of rules to be read off for every occasion,' he continued. 'It is about the ways we can meet God, can open ourselves to him, and can live as he intended us to.

'This is my message, and the Bible is full of it. To condemn me and my teaching is to deny the Bible and what is taught there.'

So ended this particular trial, as the leaders went back to reconsider, and to do some more homework. But this trial was by no means the last. Indeed, it was early on in Jesus' ministry, and relatively courteous. As time went on, and it happened again, things got less polite and more vitriolic, as is the nature with legal wrangles.

If I were writing merely for a Jewish readership, I would spend much more time on this aspect of Jesus, because as a people we dearly love trial-stories. There are many in our Bible, most of which might not even be recognised as such by a casual Western reader, but which immediately make a Jew's eyes light up with anticipation as he or she begins to read.

So what I will do instead is to summarise the main drift of the various encounters that Jesus had with the legal system, and then tell you the story of another healing which brought the trials to a close, just as they had begun with the healing at the pool of Bethesda.

Perhaps the major hearing happened about a year later at the Feast of Booths (also called 'Tabernacles' or 'Succoth'), in the October of Jesus' second and final year of ministry.

As I recounted earlier, things had changed quite a lot by

then. This was well after the events of the feeding and the sermon at Capernaum. We were no longer a popular movement, and Jesus was at pains in his preaching to make sure that his message was clearly understood, namely that he was preaching about a revolution in the moral world-order. No one could now mistake what he said as merely political, although when he talked about love, as opposed to power, and coming to God through him, it clearly had implications for the way politics might be done, should enough of us dare to practise what he preached.

Jesus had told his brothers that he was not going up to Jerusalem for this festival, because 'it was not his time'. In fact, he joined the rest of us about half-way through the feast. He didn't really trust his brothers, who, I think, just didn't really believe him. I suppose it's hard when you've grown up with someone to see them as from God. No doubt they remembered far too many of the usual childhood incidents to make a new and revised judgment about the grown man easy.

Everybody in Jerusalem had been talking about him, and wondering where he was, and speculation was rife. Comments varied from staunch belief in his goodness and godliness through to an equally strongly-held view that he was a cheat and a deceiver and was trying to lead people astray. There was also considerable discussion about his credentials. He was clearly a first-class teacher, but with no academic background. Where had he learnt it all?

So when Jesus did turn up, these were the questions levelled at him.

Initially the rulers kept a low profile. They wanted him out of the way, by now, but were hoping that Jesus would go too far with the people, and that there would be a lynching.

Questioning turned to Jesus' antecedents, and in a way, that was at the heart of his claims. He said that he was from God, that he was God's ambassador, God's agent. The big problem with this was that he was from Galilee, and no-one knew of any prophecies that would indicate a Northern Messiah.

Jesus just didn't think this important. It didn't matter where he was born; what mattered was where he was from, and that was God. He again called his three witnesses, and tried to get people to think through the implications.

There was no lynching, despite the hopes of the authorities, so they again intervened, sending some of the Temple police to bring him in for questioning.

We learnt from Nicodemus that there had been another discussion in the Council, provoked by the fact that the Temple police returned empty handed, and more than half-convinced by what Jesus had to say. The police came in for a tongue-lashing from their employers, who pointed out that none of the Temple hierarchy believed a word Jesus said, and nor did any of the party of reform. This was not strictly true, and Nicodemus tried to point out that they themselves would have to re-open the case if justice was to be done. He was told to go off and do some bible-study; there was no such thing as a Galilean prophet. (Sadly, Nicodemus wasn't quick enough, or perhaps learned enough, to point out that they were wrong - Jonah had come from Gath-hepher, less than three miles from Nazareth.)

It came to a head on the last day of the feast, when Jesus was in the outer court (often called 'the Court of Women') where much of the Feast of Booths centred. Part of the celebrations included bringing water up into the court from the Pool of Siloam, and pouring it out around the huge great seven-branched beacons which were lit for the festival.

Jesus stood up in the middle of the court and called out to all who would listen.

'Come to me for real water. Thirsty? Come and drink. As the Bible says, "From my heart comes living water." Drink of me and you shall live the life of eternity.'

You will note the parallel with his offer at Capernaum of living bread, and it had much the same effect.

Members of the party of reform took up the cudgels, accusing him of testifying on his own behalf. This time Jesus accepted the implications, and said that nevertheless, his witness was true.

'You don't even know where I am from,' he said, taking up the debate of the previous days, 'How can you understand the purpose for which God had sent me? God too is a witness for my defence, and if you were able to open yourselves to him, you would know this.'

Legally, Jesus was doing what is known as 'calling God to witness', and it is a legal maxim that if someone does this, his word should be accepted because God himself will take care of any perjury done in this form. To Westerners this will seem naive, but to us it is very fair. It simply is the case that people do not lie on oath when they have called God to witness, and certainly not a man like Jesus.

The reformers did not accept this, and at that point things swung round the other way. They were the ones on trial now. They had to prove that what Jesus said was false, otherwise they would find themselves judged by God himself, whose witness they had not accepted.

'If you cannot accept the word of God, and the offer that he now makes to you to come to me for life, then your existence will remain dominated by brokenness and by the fear of death,' Jesus told them. 'Fear and brokenness will lead you to destroy me, and then you will find that I am beyond your reach. You will lift me on high, but what you think of as destruction will turn out to be God's exaltation of me.'

This clash, too, ended in stalemate, with some of the crowd scandalised that the party of reform had dared to doubt the word of one calling God as witness, and others equally scandalised by what Jesus had said and implied.

But the last tussle, as in Galilee, was with those who hitherto had believed in Jesus. For them all this was just too much, in the same way as the invitation to eat his flesh and drink his blood had been earlier.

Jesus linked it with the whole question of where he was from, and broadened it to the question of where any of us are from. Changing the image from brokenness to slavery, he renewed yet again his offer of life.

'The life of eternity is the life of freedom. Why live a slave to all that binds you and hems you round; a slave to all your fears and self-centring?'

Someone among those who'd believed in him took up the thought.

'We are Abraham's children. We are not slaves and never have been.'

This was rather an odd thing to say. The children of Abraham, at least the Israelite branch, had been slaves in Egypt, in captivity in Babylon, subjugated by Alexander the Great and his heirs, and could hardly be said to be free under the Romans! But Jesus took up the intention of the speaker, namely that Abraham offers a special relationship with God to his descendants.

'Physical birth has nothing to do with it. It's not where or from whom we're born that matters, but how we behave. Abraham's children are those who act like Abraham. He was a man of faith.'

'You claim you are from God,' came the reply, 'but we are all children of God.'

'Then do the deeds of God, as I do,' said Jesus. 'At the moment you are opposing God, and acting more like his adversary in court - that's your moral paternity right now!'

Stung by this, several of them flung counter-accusations back.

'You're acting like a Samaritan!' (Water off a duck's back to Jesus, he was not rabidly anti-Samaritan as so many of my countrymen are, and had quite a bit of time for their theology.)

'You say we speak like the adversary? You're the one possessed by a demon!'

'For doing the will of God? For offering life? Hear the word of truth,' said Jesus. 'Anyone who accepts me cannot be bound, even by death itself.'

For many of them, this simply reinforced their belief that he was indeed mad, and that they had been mistaken in him.

Jesus continued, 'The life of eternity transcends death. Such life unites all who trust in God, living and departed, including Abraham.'

'Are you claiming Abraham as a recipient of this life you offer, then?'

Jesus replied, 'Hear then the word of truth. Before all people of God, before Abraham himself, I am.'

This was an unmistakable use of the divine 'I am', and they immediately picked up stones. It looked as if the lynching hoped for by the rulers was about to happen.

Jesus simply gazed calmly at them. It was the eye contact that did it. They dropped their eyes from his as he looked at each individual, and then they started glancing sideways at each other. Clearly everyone was waiting for someone else to throw the first stone.

Jesus then walked slowly and calmly straight up to them, and they parted to let him through. He continued walking, and left the Temple.

This was the last time Jesus himself was tried; that is, according to our law.

In these trials, Jesus had taken the idea of judgment, as we Jews understand it, and given it deeper and deeper significance. Effectively, what he was saying was that each of us makes our own judgment - in both senses of that phrase. Where we are from and our habits of thought and lifestyle do not necessarily have to bind us. We can break out of these by an act of choice. That is the judgment we make. Having made this judgment (which, of course, is usually a process over time, not a one-off event), it in turn judges us. By this Jesus meant that the choices we make lead to the way we see life and the fullness to which we live it. In the life of eternity, which it is open to everyone to choose, the events that happen to us, the relationships we make, the person we become, are all a part of an open and joyful acceptance that puts everything, even physical death, in perspective. Life, with all its ups and downs, becomes a whole experience rather than a lot of broken bits.

In a nutshell: 'We make our own judgment.'

Jesus' message was that this is good news, because our judgment can be as forgiving and as life-enhancing as we choose, because God is on our side, and acceptance of Jesus enables us to tap into this.

There was a sequel to this series of trials, which ended as they had begun, with a healing and a pool, and it followed hard on the heels of the events I have just described. It was, of course, another sign, and one that was not lost on the authorities.

Jerusalem has its share of beggars, and often more than its share, because of the responsibilities laid on us by our Law to give to the poor.

One of these was a man who had been born blind, a curse which it was difficult to explain as being his own fault; he could hardly have brought it upon himself in the womb. We asked Jesus about this, and he replied as follows:

'You don't really think that every misfortune in life is deserved, do you? Illness may or may not be self-inflicted, but something like this certainly isn't. No more can you blame his parents. God, who has an open and true heart, would hardly punish the child for what the parent had done. These things are part of the brokenness of the world itself.'

'So what should this man do? Accept it?' asked tender-hearted Andrew.

'He seems to do so,' smiled Jesus, touched by Andrew's concern. 'In this case, however, it could be that an unveiling awaits - of his eyes, and of the love of God. He is in the right place at the right time.'

Out came Jesus' favourite proverb again, 'There are twelve daylight hours, and twelve dark,' and then he said, 'This one is wise enough, in his darkness, to walk in the day.' He added, 'I am. I am the light of day.'

He went over to the man, and got him to squat down beside him at the side of the road. Jesus spat in the dust, and kneaded it to make a gooey paste-like mess, and then, with a caress of affection, he smeared the mess all over the man's eyes, smoothing it gently into and around the sightless eyes in their sockets.

'There,' he said. 'I send you away now. You are sent to 'Sent Pool'. Wash the stuff off and return.' ('Sent Pool' is the literal meaning of 'Siloam'.)

When the blind man had tapped his way with his stick down the long ridge of the lower city, and negotiated the steep descent at its bottom end into the pool, he got someone to lead him down the steps to the water, where, we were told later, he simply plunged his whole head under the surface, and shook it, so that Jesus' muddy paste just peeled off and drifted down and away. When he lifted his head out of the water, he could see perfectly.

For what happened next, I am indebted in part to the man himself, who later told us his story, but more especially to my relative the priestly official, who took some notes. Apparently the priests realised that the reform party were holding a trial of the man, and sent my relative to keep an eye on them.

The man's return into the city caused quite a stir, so much so that some of his nearest and dearest weren't even sure if it were he. The real problem, however, turned out to be that it was the Sabbath, again, and when the man inadvertently described Jesus' paste-making as 'kneading', the reformers were down on him like a ton of bricks. Kneading is one of those activities that they had specifically proscribed, originally to make sure women didn't have to cook on their day off, but now they treated it as another restriction on all sorts of things which even included children making mud pies!

Just as they had originally charged Jesus as an accessory to Sabbath-breaking, in the case of the bed-carrying, so now they charged the poor man with the same charge as an accessory to kneading.

They asked him to describe exactly what had happened, which he did, and then asked for his comment on a healer plying his trade on the Sabbath.

'Healer?' replied the man, 'Surely more than that. He must at least be a prophet. You see, I didn't become blind, I was *born* that way.'

This was an important point, as the man could not only see for the first time, but he could also understand what his eyes were telling him. If you like, he had been given not only sight, but insight as well. Insight, of course, belongs to God.

The reform people conferred together, and decided that they wanted proof of this, and so there was an adjournment while the parents were fetched.

The reformers were very angry about the whole thing. Originally, they thought that they had found something that they could use against Jesus. (In this they were deluding themselves. People didn't care half as much about their Sabbath rules as the hardliners thought. They had the fanatics' belief that everyone shared their agenda.) However, it was already out of hand. Their chief witness was talking about 'a prophet', and the healing had turned out to be something more. They had hoped that the accused would be more pliable, as the bed-carrier had been, and their intention had been to drop the charge against him if he would testify against Jesus.

Fourth Witness

The reformers were never very good at keeping their plans to themselves (unlike the much more politically-aware priestly aristocrats), and by the time the parents had been found, it was pretty generally known that the reform party were out for blood.

The man's parents, when they appeared, were obviously well aware of this, and frightened of the reformers, who recently had even been excluding people who fell foul of them from the synagogues under their control.

The parents were asked to identify their son, which they did, and testify that he had been blind at birth, which, reluctantly, they also did. But no other question would they answer.

'If he was blind from birth, how can he now see?' they were asked.

'Ask him,' they replied.

'You must have a theory, at least?'

'No. No. We don't know anything about it. He's a full grown adult, and we're not responsible for him.'

'But he is your son?'

'Fully grown up. You can't blame us. Ask him for an explanation.'

The parents' evident fear, and their readiness to throw their own flesh and blood to the lions, were doing the accusers no good. None of us like any sign of intimidation in legal matters; we see that as belonging to the law-courts of the Greeks and the Romans. So the parents were dismissed, and attention re-focused on our new-visioned hero.

'Your new-found sight is a gift direct from God,' they told him. 'Your so-called healer is a Sabbath-breaker. You must thank God and not him.'

'A subtle distinction,' replied the man, 'too deep for me. What I do know is that now I can see. I am very grateful for that.' He didn't make it clear whether he was grateful to God, or to Jesus, or to both.

They took him for a second time through the details of what had happened, trying to trip him up or get him to incriminate Jesus in some way. The man was getting impatient, and plainly felt that he owed Jesus a debt that he could express in loyalty. He was in stark contrast to his parents, and one wondered how two such mice had produced a lion.

When they proposed to go over it yet again, he had had enough.

'I've told you often enough, now. I'm beginning to suspect you love the story so much that you want to sign up among his followers.'

His admiration for Jesus was clear to all, and the reformers decided to warn him of the dangers of this.

'You sound dangerously like a follower of this law-breaker yourself,' said one of them in a silkily menacing tone. 'We, of course, are true followers of Moses, as you should be. God speaks through Moses, not some unknown Northerner from God knows where.'

'Wonderful!' replied the man, who was getting braver by the minute. 'God knows where and you don't! I'll stick with God, I think. If you want 'unknown', it's 'unknown' to heal someone like me, blind from birth. That's an act of God, and God must listen hard and close to this Jesus, to do what he asks in this way.'

You can imagine the effect that this had on the reform party. From their point of view the whole thing had gone wrong. Their intended witness was witnessing, all right, he was virtually prophesying, but for the defence, not for the prosecution. They had to extract themselves as best they could, but their closing shot was petty and unworthy.

'You dare to lecture us in theology?' their spokesman said. 'You who have been cursed with an affliction from birth? Don't think your curse is over. We now curse you and exclude you from our synagogues.'

They didn't control all the synagogues, by any means, and

there would be plenty of reformers who would not have agreed with this judgment, but even so it was a mean piece of spite, and when Jesus heard of it, he went to find the man. Jesus was impressed by the contrast between this man and the cripple he had healed at the pool of Bethesda, and saw in him a man who wanted to make his own choices and judgments about life. When he found him he asked him about this.

'Would you like to meet one who can link the things of time and eternity; who can open to you life lived in the freedom of your own choosing, however risky?'

'Indeed I would!' replied the man. 'Who is it?'

He clearly knew the answer to this, but was following the lead that Jesus had set in his question.

'You know,' said Jesus. 'I am he. You see me with the eyes in your head and the eyes of your heart. God has opened both for you.'

'I believe,' said the man, kneeling before Jesus.

Jesus gave him a blessing. 'God has given you a wise and discerning heart. And indeed, it is for the sake of discernment that God sends me to you and to the world. I discern between blind and sighted, so that they can discern God in me.'

This was overheard by some of the reform party, who took it personally, and asked if he meant them.

'I suppose you count us among the undiscerning blind,' one of them said.

'That is your choice,' said Jesus, 'The choice always belongs to you alone.

'Being blind is no shame. But being blind and saying "I can see. Follow me." is dangerous and wicked folly.'

The powers that be had set out initially to judge Jesus, and things had now come full circle. By making this reply, Jesus had shown how they were the ones judged, and that they had brought the judgment on themselves.

Chapter 11

Back in the Upper Room, Jesus had reached the point where he was ready to tell us in more detail about leaving us.

The failures of the authorities to deal with him either by trial or by lynching meant that they had to resort to guile, and while we didn't understand in the way Jesus did just how close the crisis was, yet we were all uneasy. His talk of 'exaltation', which could, in black humour, mean being lifted up onto a cross, was one of the several hints he had been dropping about what was to happen.

Jesus knew the question was in our hearts, and indeed people had been talking about it on the couches and at the other tables. The odd whisper had drifted up to Jesus and myself on the top couch in the interludes when the jugs had been going round or when we had paused to eat or to refill our plates.

'What does he mean about going away?'

'Humiliation and exaltation, and tomorrow?'

'Is he returning to God?' This was Nathaniel, who was still waiting for the vision Jesus had promised him when they first met.

'I still don't see why I can't go with him.' As you've guessed, this was our Rock, hurt and frightened by Jesus' prophecy, and all the more determined not to desert him.

'You're discussing my going, aren't you?' said Jesus. 'I know it's confusing - now you see me, now you don't, and then you will.

'You will be bereft and leaderless, and won't know what has come to you. It will seem like disaster to you, but you will be on your own in that. The rulers will be delighted; I shall have been "dealt with" at last.

'But will I? Your pain will be no more than birth-pangs, for I shall return to you renewed. As some of the women here know, there is nothing like the joy of a new baby, it makes all the pain and effort seem like nothing.' He paused, with a smiling glance at the mothers in the room. 'So they tell me.'

He went on, 'It will be like that for you.

'This is beyond the understanding of the powerful and those who are merely wise in the ways of the world.'

'So are you going to return to us, and to no-one else?' asked Judas. This was the other Judas, we had two of them in the band, or had had until an hour or so ago. The coincidence of name reminded me of our treasurer, and I wondered uneasily where he was, and what he was doing in his hurt and hate.

'I shall be with you and with whoever chooses the path of love, just as my father will be,' Jesus answered him. 'As I showed you with the vine tree, we shall be sharing a united life together.'

'You feel deserted, but if I don't go, then my Spirit cannot come to you,' Jesus continued.

'I promised you a friend, and my Spirit will be that Friend. He will stand by you in your trials, He will help you understand all the things I've said to you, and remind you of all the ones you didn't notice or have forgotten.'

He smiled at us, his smile saying 'Don't think that I don't know how hard it is for you to take all of this in, or even the smallest part of it.'

He went on, 'The Spirit, the Friend, will always be there for you, helping you to stand up to those in power, helping you to make wise choices, helping you to discover the life of eternity. He will point you to me and to the excitement of God. And there will be no leaving you friendless again.'

As well as the word 'Spirit', itself not an easy one, Jesus was using a Greek word, 'Paraclete', for 'Friend'. It was a word that was coming into use because we didn't have quite that concept in our own language. It means someone who stands beside you when you are on trial. Not a paid counsel or a lawyer; as I have said, we think those a bad idea, but a staunch ally and support. This was the sort of picture Jesus was painting for us.

He himself took up the word 'Friend' and shifted to a more familiar idea of friendship.

'We have talked about master and servant, teacher and pupil, tonight,' he said. 'I have a better word for our relationship. We are friends. You are my friends and I am yours. Friendship can lead to the greatest love of all - being willing to die for each other. This is my gift to you.'

He had one more thing to add about the Friend, linked no doubt to the idea of standing in court.

'When you receive my Spirit-Friend, he will be another witness to me, and sharing with you will enable you to be my witnesses too.'

This was not easy to take in at that time. We were thoroughly frightened and apprehensive, and the last thing we could imagine was going out and arguing with the priests and the reform party in the Temple, or preaching in the synagogues. Jesus knew how we were feeling, and let us have another rest before his last piece of teaching.

He relaxed back on the couch, and swung himself round the other way so that he could lean on me for a bit. A hum of discussion had begun around us.

'That last comment, Beloved,' he said to me quietly, 'I know it is too much for you now, but don't forget it. Remember my three witnesses? John, the signs and Moses? The time will come when I shall need a fourth witness.'

Chapter 12

As there is a pause, I shall take the opportunity to tell you of two earlier conversations when Jesus talked about the Spirit and that go back close to the beginning of his ministry.

One was in Jerusalem with a senior male aristocrat, and the other, in complete (and shocking) contrast, with a Samaritan, and, moreover, a woman.

Jesus' dealings with women were unprecedented, and, for us disciples, very difficult to stomach. He treated women in just the same way as if they were men. He argued and discussed with them, and even listened to their opinions with respect. In some ways, Jesus went even further than this, choosing to share some of the key moments in his life with women rather than with men. I have to admit that, on the whole, the women come rather better out of the story of Jesus than us men. The stark contrast in the story I am about to tell you is a good example of this.

So to the first part of the story, which happened shortly after Jesus had disrupted the stallholders in the Temple, and had come so dramatically to the notice of the authorities.

Jesus was staying in my family's house in Jerusalem, as was generally known, and one evening, after the meal and quite late, too late for decent people to be roaming the streets, there was a knock at the door.

Not wanting to leave it to one of the servants at that time of night, I went myself to see who it was, and found one of the most respected men in Jerusalem standing there. It was, in fact, none other than Nicodemus, one of the ruling priestly party, but also, as occasionally was the case, a member of the reform party.

There were several aristocrats who were unhappy with the slackness, as they saw it, of the Temple hierarchy, and who

101

had attached themselves to one or the other of the reforming teachers in the hope of improving things from within, so to speak. Nicodemus was one of those. You might say, he represented in himself both of the power groups that were to prove so inimical to Jesus.

Nicodemus and I knew each other distantly; our families moved in roughly the same circles in Jerusalem. He asked if he might come in and visit Jesus.

I took him up onto the roof, where we were relaxing after dinner, wondering if he was acting as a messenger from the powers that be, and what such a message might mean. It became very clear, however, that this secret and night-time visit was made entirely on his own account. Nicodemus approached Jesus in the most respectful and honorific tones, and began by addressing Jesus with his own title of 'Rabbi'.

'Teacher,' he said, 'Many of us can see God at work in you. The things you say, the things you do... Godly, clearly... God's work...' He must have had the speech prepared, but as he looked down at Jesus, seated at his ease, and glinting up at him in what little lamplight there was (the night was overcast), the words dried on his lips.

Jesus smiled, the amusement flickering in his eyes, and waved him down onto another stool. Nicodemus took it, and accepted the beaker of wine that I put into his hand. Jesus then came straight to the point.

'New start, Nicodemus,' he said. 'New birth. That's what you need. You've done too well in the ways of the world, and it's tying you down. You need to be born again into the world of truth, into the life of eternity. This is a word of truth.'

This was not what Nicodemus expected, of course. Maybe he had imagined a deep conversation, Rabbi to Rabbi, or the sharing of plans for the improvement of the Temple, the nation, or even the world. He had certainly not expected to be told that he was on the wrong track altogether, and needed to start again. With Rabbi-like precision, he started to analyse what Jesus had said.

'I am a grown man, now,' he began, rather ponderously. 'Too big for a womb, and in any case, no-one can undo their actual experience, and return to the innocence and ignorance of the fœtus...'

Jesus cut across him; he was not going to get trapped into a nit-picking theological debate.

'This is a word of truth,' he said, the authority of his tone contrasting with Nicodemus' academic style. 'The things of God, the life of eternity, these are entered by a new birth as life-changing as our natural birth. Baptism is a good sign for it, but it is a matter of the Spirit.'

The word 'Spirit' hung in the air between them. Nicodemus looked a little hurt at Jesus' cavalier treatment of him, but to do him justice, he was more interested in the concept Jesus offered that in any hurt dignity. 'Spirit', and especially '*the* Spirit' was one of those ideas that can take us to the heart of things, but it is also a very slippery word, as Jesus showed in his next offering.

'Matter for material things, that's important for the world we see. But we need to keep the distinctions clear. The Spirit for spiritual things. Everything we can see and touch can be taken to bits, including our born bodies. But when we've done that, the truth has been lost from it. The truth comes from the world of eternity, it blows like a whirlwind through the world that we see, and we can hold it in our hands no more than we can hold the wind of the desert. That's the Spirit.'

Jesus was holding his left hand in front of him, palm upwards as he spoke, with his fingers closing on the air. The gesture showed the futility of trying to seize the wind.

'People re-born of the Spirit know this. They may hold the wind in their hands, for they don't try with the hands of flesh.' His hand was open again, and this time seemed to be full of something real and palpable, but just beyond our sight.

'Yes,' said Nicodemus, slowly, 'I understand the

distinction. I understand your words.' A pause, and then the real question, showing at the same time both his spiritual yearning, and his fear of surrendering what he had achieved.

'But in practical terms... How?'

'You're the rabbi! One of our nation's best!' Jesus teased Nicodemus, 'and here am I instructing you in quite simple practical matters. If you don't accept this, then can you accept God?'

Nicodemus spread his hands in a gesture both of resignation and, in a curious way, of willingness to learn.

Jesus explained.

'God is love. His Spirit fills the universe with love. You can't see it, touch it or feel it, so how can you know it? God sends me to show it to you. Trust me. The choice is yours; is open to everyone. How you decide will go to make up who you are and what you can choose to be. What do you really want?'

Nicodemus saw that. He also felt the challenge deeply. For him such a choice could lead him eventually to lose all his hard-won authority and respect in the councils of the nation. It could mean that he would be marginalised, a laughing-stock, scorned by all his closest friends whose good opinion he dearly wanted to keep. To do this was a terrible risk to take; a terrifying price to pay. Was it worth it?

It would take time to think this through; some years, in fact, in Nicodemus' case. He bade us a courteous, thoughtful, and rather wistful 'good evening'. He left, as he had come, in the dark of the night.

A few weeks later, we were heading north. We had spent some time with John, baptising. We were exercising what you might call a parallel ministry, and many were coming. (You will have noticed that Jesus mentioned the usefulness of baptism as a first step to Nicodemus.) But it began to be misunderstood. People thought that we were in opposition;

two rival camps, as it were, and people were also thinking of baptism as an end in itself; a ritual purification.

We decided to go up to Galilee, leaving John to continue on his own.

John was sorry to see Jesus go, as he had been energetically encouraging people to regard Jesus as the prophesied Messiah. John had cast himself in the role of 'best man' to Jesus' 'bridegroom', using a common biblical picture of the life of eternity as God's great wedding feast.

John also talked very much in terms of the Spirit, but with a much better grasp of the idea than the learned Nicodemus, and he pointed to Jesus as the one who would share this Spirit with us.

We went north by way of Samaria. Jesus was interested, among other things, in the ruins of the great Samaritan temple on Mount Gerazim, and on the way he told us something of Samaritan theology. He seemed to know more about this than was quite respectable for a Jewish teacher!

He explained to us how, at the time when our people had returned from Babylon, they had come back to find many Jews who had not been deported, and had remained in the land. These had continued to worship God. But the returning Jews thought that they had allowed a certain amount of paganism to creep in from the five religions of the peoples the Babylonians had sent to live with them. (The Babylonian empire had ruled by means of mass deportations, which weakened people's natural loyalties, and made them less likely to revolt.) Those who had stayed in the land had tried to work with the returning Jews, but found it impossible. In particular, the returnees had wanted their priests especially to divorce any wife that was not of provable pure blood. The leading home priest, Manasseh, was deeply in love with his wife, Nicaso, and refused. Nicaso's father happened to be no less than the local Babylonian governor, and he offered to build another temple on Mount Gerazim for all those who wouldn't accept the strict (and unbiblical) rules of the returnees. Manasseh was delighted, and became the first high priest of the Samaritans.

The way Jesus told it, the returning Jews sounded not a little like our party of reform. When Nathaniel suggested this, Jesus looked sideways at him and nodded slowly.

He told us that the Samaritans only accepted the Law, the first five books of the Bible; no different from our priestly party. But he went on to say that Samaritans would have nothing to do with Jerusalem, or indeed with anything that suggested the primacy of the Temple there. They were expecting the Messiah promised by Moses, and hoped for a prophet, not a king in the style of David. Jesus, of course, had a lot of sympathy with this, but regretted that they refused to use the insights of the great prophets.

This was all new and strange to us, as Jews are used to thinking the worst of Samaritans. We are supposed to avoid them and never speak to them, and they are regarded as the lowest of the low; renegade Jews who have become mongrels and denied God. Jesus, as always, didn't accept something just because everybody thought it, especially when it was based on hatred and prejudice.

The Samaritan temple had been destroyed about a hundred and fifty years ago, by a high priest from Jerusalem, although worship had continued in the ruins.

It was Jesus' interest in the Samaritans and their ruined temple that had led us this way, instead of one of the usual routes to the north avoiding Samaritan territory. By midday we found ourselves a mile or so south of their main city, Sychar (which many call Shechem). Mount Gerazim towered up on our left hand, and beyond it Mount Ebal, the famous mountain of the curse. The moment you saw them, you could see the contrast between the fertile and beckoning mount of blessing and the rocky, dark and arid mountain just topping it behind.

Fourth Witness

We stopped where there was some shade by a well at the side of the road. We had been walking since early in the morning, having camped overnight in the hills of Ephraim. The night had been hot and sticky, and we had little with us for breakfast, hence our early start.

Jesus was feeling tired, and said he would like to stay there, if the rest of us didn't mind going to do some very necessary bartering in Sychar. Ordinarily we would have jibbed at this, but our views of the Samaritans had been shaken by the morning's discussion, and so we agreed to go and see what we could find in the way of provisions.

I heard the story of what happened next from both protagonists, and I really wish I could have been a fly on the wall.

Jesus was leaning against the well, sitting on the low wall that encircled it, enjoying the shade and a chance to sit and simply 'be' for a bit. After a while he heard the scuffing of sandals approaching, and at first assumed it was one of us. Then the noise stopped, and he opened one eye.

About ten yards away, and regarding him with the utmost suspicion, was a Samaritan woman with a water pot on her shoulder. She was clearly at a loss, as she wanted to use the well, but equally, did not want to go any nearer someone who was suspicious on three counts. He was a stranger, he was a man, and he was a Jew.

'Ah, a water pot,' said Jesus. 'Could you give me a drink?'

The woman's expression turned from suspicion to surprise.

'I don't know you,' she said, amazed that he should be willing to speak to her.

'Very true,' said Jesus.

'But you're a Jew,' she said.

'I think I knew that,' he smiled at her.

'And a man.'

'Guilty,' he laughed, 'but I am a very thirsty male Jew.'

'I don't know you,' she said again, but drew nearer, clearly wondering how improper it would be for her to give him some water.

'If you did know me,' said Jesus, 'you'd be asking me for water. I could give you a really life-saving drink.'

'Hardly,' the woman laughed back, infected by his humour. 'The well is very deep, and you have nothing to draw it out with. Anyway, you can't possibly improve on the water of *this* well.'

'Why is that?' asked Jesus.

'Jacob, one of the greatest of our ancestors, provided this well,' she said, 'and used it for himself and all his people and flocks. It is famous throughout the world. You can scarcely claim to be greater than Jacob.'

Jesus knew from this that he was dealing with one who was interested in more than just history. Hidden in what she said was the claim to be truly descended from Jacob (whose other name was Israel, and from whom our nation is named). She had, in fact, made the traditional Samaritan attack on Jewish exclusivism.

Jesus replied, 'Even Jacob's water leaves you thirsty again. I can supply water that lifts you above and beyond thirst. I'm talking about true thirst; the thirst for life with God.'

'A big claim,' she responded. 'Give me your water, and we'll see if indeed I never need to draw water from this well again. Show me that, and I'll be happy to talk with you about God.'

'Talk about God?' said Jesus. 'Can you show me your god? Can you bring him here?'

'I have no god of that sort,' said the woman impatiently. 'You think I am a pagan, to keep a household god in a cupboard beside my hearth?'

'Well said!' Jesus replied. 'You Samaritans are supposed to have five gods, but clearly these are not yours. You are a seeker after a new way of understanding God himself, are you not? That is what I offer.'

'If this is true,' she said, 'then you are a prophet. Tell me, prophet, where should we worship God?'

Jesus smiled at the theological trap she was setting him, impressed at the same time with her seeking.

She continued, 'Two temples. One on this mountain.' She waved across at Gerazim as she spoke. 'Ruined now, but we still use it.' They both knew who had destroyed it. 'The other in Jerusalem. One God, but two temples and two factions so sure of their opposing claims.'

Jesus was touched by her way of expressing the traditional rivalry, and gave her a full and straight answer.

'God is beyond place. Place merely helps us to focus on him, whether there, or here. Do not dismiss us Jews. God has given himself especially to us; not as our property but as our gift to the world. You are right about claim and counter-claim.

'Your temple is in ruins; do you suppose the one in Jerusalem will stand much longer? The time is coming... No, the time has come, when our encounter with God will be anywhere. If you want to name a place, then it will be in the heart of God himself, in his Spirit. That is the truth of the matter, and sharing in life with God is all about truth.'

There was silence for a moment as she digested this, realising that Jesus was talking about a new age taking up both Samaritan and Jew, and transcending present belief and practice.

Then she said slowly, 'We believe that a Messiah is soon to come, and I think you Jews do too.' She looked at him with a question in her eyes.

Jesus nodded in answer. 'I am,' he said, and the name was not lost on her. 'I, the Jewish man who speaks to a Samaritan woman, I am he.'

It was at this moment that we returned. Not perhaps the best of timing. The woman, who, as the conversation progressed, had so far forgotten herself as to sit beside Jesus on the coping of the well, saw us approach and jumped to her feet, embarrassed, but at the same time full of excitement at what Jesus had just said. He had chimed in with her natural wondering and seeking, and she had an open wisdom that allowed her to accept his claim.

She looked at him with a light in her eyes, glanced sheepishly at us, and then with a muttered word to Jesus indicating that she was going for her friends and that he was to stay with her pot and look after it until she got back, she was off.

We watched her figure diminished by the distance as she went up the road to Sychar, half walking, half trotting, almost skipping at times.

The fact that we had to wait until she was out of earshot gave us time to think.

Some of us, Nathaniel for example, were angry that Jesus should risk his reputation and ours in this way. The fact that it was very unlikely that there were any Jews within miles to tell the tale didn't change things in the slightest.

Some of us were embarrassed. Peter had gone a dull brick-red and was looking everywhere except at Jesus, and wondering just how we could get over the uncomfortable moment. Catching Jesus with a woman, and a Samaritan at that, was a bit like walking in on a naked guest, to Peter. Least said, soonest mended.

Andrew, always the most accepting of us, was clearly trying to make excuses for Jesus in his mind. Maybe she had been in need, or suffered an accident, and turned to Jesus for help and protection. Or maybe...

Significantly, it was to Andrew that Jesus addressed his next remark, although it was also meant for all of us.

'Another seeker, like yourself, Andrew,' and he nodded at the woman disappearing up the road. 'What was your first action after we had met?'

Caught off-balance at the unexpected question, Andrew answered in a surprised tone, 'Well, I brought Peter to you...' Unconsciously he reached out for his brother's elbow as if he were about to present him again to Jesus.

'And Philip brought me Nathaniel,' said Jesus. 'Let's see what my new disciple brings.'

It was, in the early days, a shock to hear Jesus refer to women as his disciples, and this was a double shock, given her race and religion. Peter, desperate to change the subject, found his tongue.

'Have something to eat, teacher. You must be starving.' He made it sound almost as if hunger could excuse Jesus' behaviour.

'Oh, I'm well satisfied, thank you,' grinned Jesus, amused at Peter's embarrassment, and reaching out an affectionate hand for Peter to pull him up off the low wall.

'Has someone been giving you food?' asked Nathaniel. He didn't say it, but you could hear the words 'that woman' in his voice.

'God and I have been working together,' Jesus replied. 'That is meat and drink to me.' This was certainly true. Nothing revitalised Jesus like an encounter, especially a theological one.

Then he continued, 'Now stop and think. Andrew brought me Peter, Philip brought me Nathaniel, the woman who just left will return with her friends. There is no difference. A questing soul is a questing soul. A disciple who brings more disciples is a good disciple. I suspect that she is about to bring many. A small seed for such a rich harvest. Sooner or later, you will be engaged on the same work, and then I hope you remember this early missionary.'

Then he reverted to his conversation with Nicodemus. 'You remember our reforming aristocrat? He isn't here with us, is he? He is tied down by the fear of human approval. It matters more to him than the approval of God. It is human approval that worries you when you make these distinctions of Jew and Samaritan, woman and man.'

He smiled at Nathaniel, who had started to shake his head.

'Now come on, Nathaniel,' Jesus laughed. 'Weren't you thinking, "What would people say, if they knew?"'

Nathaniel smiled back ruefully, and as Jesus continued to laugh, could not help himself but join in. Nathaniel was always a bit serious about his theology, and it was a good sign when he laughed. You knew he'd got the point, then.

The laughter spread, washing away the tension, and welding us together again as a group. It was not the last time that Jesus had to make this point, as habits take a long time to die. Even towards the end Nathaniel would be quite shocked when Jesus waved him to silence so that he could listen to Martha in a theological discussion. Nevertheless, gradually Jesus taught us to share as a community of equals, as far as possible within a society that regarded it as both shocking and unnatural.

It was, therefore, a laughing and joyful group of Jewish men that the Samaritan woman found on her return. She looked at us in some surprise. Not Jesus, of whom she had almost instantly learnt to expect anything, but the rest of us, whom she had left suspicious and embarrassed.

She had brought with her considerable numbers of friends and neighbours, agog to see Jesus.

'What have you been saying about me?' he teased her, but she had a ready reply.

'Nothing much,' she said. 'Only that you told me my life story, can answer anything they care to ask, and are in all probability the Messiah.'

Our laughter as they approached had done more than anything to put the new arrivals at their ease, at least provisionally, and the woman's light and joyful reply also helped. In no time at all Jesus was in the midst of a question-

and-answer session very different from the ones we were used to in Jerusalem. It was full of life and of openness. Ideas and hopes were flying about like confetti in the wind of the Spirit, and Jesus was being taken to the hearts of the people of Sychar as if he were the answer to all their dreams. Not surprising - they understood that he was.

They begged us to stay, and we did, for two days. When we finally continued our journey north, we left behind a group of followers of Jesus that had already begun to explore the life of eternity and to share it with one another.

I have never forgotten that group, not of Jews but of Samaritans. Nor have I forgotten that their founder was the stranger woman at the well, and that the rest of us would have ignored her entirely. Jesus had pointed us to the contrast between her and Nicodemus, and it is a lesson I keep in my heart. I am constantly learning it again as I slip back into worrying over what people think about me or what I'm expected to think about others.

Chapter 13

In the Upper Room, our long learning was coming to a close.

'There is one final thing that I need to say to you,' Jesus continued after a while. 'Indeed, I have been saying it all evening.'

The hum of our separate, uneasy and nervous conversations subsided, and we turned again to look at Jesus, who had swung his legs forward, so that he could sit upright on our couch, with his feet on the floor in front of him.

'I am not a law-giver,' said Jesus, 'but I do give you one new commandment. Remember how I washed your feet as a sign to you, and what I said then. It is the hardest of one of all.

'You are to love one another.'

He pointed round at us to emphasise this.

'Harder than loving those you chance upon. Harder than loving God. Look at the faces of your friends in this room. You are to love each other. We know each other so well now, all our little habits and foibles. That is the raw material of love. God knows you inside out, as I know you, and loves all that he sees. You are to love like that.

'Such love changes people. It can be seen in their faces and in their actions. Gradually the mark of love will etch itself onto you, and all will be able to see it. The mark of those who are mine, who are God's.'

He lent forward, urgency in his voice as he made sure we understood.

'I have given you an example. Live in love and you will find that you are already at the heart of the life of eternity. You will be one with God and one with me.'

His own love for us was shining in his face as he looked round at us again, seeing and marking each individual.

'Live that way and all things become possible for you. You have marvelled at my signs, not always for the right reasons, true,' (with a smile at Lazarus, here) 'but believe me, they are as nothing to what you can do if you really live in love. The life of eternity is a life crammed full of things quite beyond the ways of the world.'

Some of the signs I had seen went through my mind. The bread, the wine, the gift of sight, the foot washing. They were all about giving. They had been those moments when Jesus had opened a window for us into the heart of God, and he was now asking us to do the same for others. He continued, as if in answer to my thought.

'I have begun the work. You are to continue it. I have offered life to all, but only touched a few. You will touch many, many, and through you they will touch me.

'You are my friends, chosen ones just as I am God's chosen one. Loved by God and at the heart of his work for the world. I come from God, and now leave you to return to him. I die for you, but our friendship will be stronger than death.'

After so much that was so difficult to understand, a sense of relief ran round the room. Not at the thought of Jesus' death, which to be honest I think we still did not believe, but at the clarity with which Jesus spoke. There was a moment of easing of the tension, and people helped themselves to a few grapes or a handful of olives. Mary of Magdala was behind our couch, refilling Jesus' goblet and mine.

'Ah, yes,' said someone from one of the tables down the other end of the room. 'That is clear. Of course you came from God and must sometime return to him.'

'Hold that thought,' replied Jesus, 'for tonight I shall be deserted by you all.' His pointing finger swept from Thomas on our right and round the room to Andrew at this end of the

115

left-hand couch. I glanced at Peter, who had his head down, looking at the couch on which he lay.

'But God will be with me,' Jesus continued, 'so I shall not be alone.'

None of us knew how to reply to this repeated accusation of desertion, but after a moment Jesus moved on to his final sentence.

'Courage,' he said, 'I have already as good as won, in the life of eternity. Your turn will come, and you will then know what I mean.

'Love one another, and that love will conquer the world.'

He paused again, and then, swinging back onto the couch to recline, made the move that would finish the meal.

'Let us pray,' he said.

Chapter 14

As the evening had progressed, Jesus had said more and more about what we were to do in the future. As you have seen, this was in terms of ourselves going on to share the life of eternity with all people.

Although Jesus had spent his entire ministry within the boundaries of what had been Israel, he had talked on several occasions of the people beyond. In any case, he had always made it clear that the life of eternity was for everyone.

There had been a practical demonstration of his care for pagans as soon as we arrived in Galilee after our encounter with the woman in Samaria. This happened when one of Herod's many foreign officials had heard of Jesus' return, and personally made the trip to Cana from Capernaum to ask for help.

He had strained every nerve to cover the ground as fast as he could, for he had set off as soon as it was light enough, and arrived in Cana not long after noon, having walked a fraction over twenty miles, including the ascent up the Valley of the Doves.

He found us as soon as he arrived, for we were sitting at the gate, resting ourselves from our own journeyings of the previous days.

Without so much as an introduction, he blurted out his request.

'Jesus, my son is about to die. He has a burning fever and we've tried everything. Please come to Capernaum and make him better.'

There was a stir around the gate. It was as if the crowd were ready for the latest cure as if it were a sideshow at a circus. Jesus flashed a look almost of contempt at their attitude.

'The latest marvel!' he exclaimed. 'That's all you're interested in. So long as it entertains, who cares what it really means.'

The official became even more distressed. Did this mean a refusal by Jesus?

'Master, come! Now!' he pleaded. 'Before it's too late.'

Jesus looked up at him from where he was sitting, with the man bending anxiously over him. The sweat from his journey was still running down his face in rivulets, and his pain and love were plain to see.

'It's all right,' said Jesus gently. 'Your son is better.'

A look of doubt crossed the man's face, but Jesus gazed steadily at him, waiting for him to speak. He said nothing, but his whole demeanour changed. He stretched out his hand to touch Jesus, and then let it fall without completing the gesture. He bowed to him, slowly, and at last said just two words.

'Thank you.'

'You'll want to be on your way, then,' Jesus smiled at him.

'Yes indeed,' he said, and left.

We heard later that he managed just over half the journey back before night overtook him, and the following morning he was met by members of his household just near Magdala, as he reached the lake-side. They told him that the boy had made a total recovery, beginning just after noon on the previous day.

The pagan official had heard Jesus' words about 'the latest marvel', and when he had time to think about them, he began to see the sign as a whole. He became one of us, in a manner of speaking, as did some of his people.

The most significant moment, however, in terms of Jesus and the wider world, happened as recently as the day before our last meal in the Upper Room.

Fourth Witness

Some Greeks had arrived in Jerusalem for the Passover. They were what we called 'God-trusters', which means that they were not ethnic Jews, but ready to believe in God and to adopt Jewish customs and theology. They had heard about Jesus and were curious. Indeed, they were more than curious, because they had heard enough to think that Jesus might be able to offer them what they were seeking. Non-Jews, however devout, would always be second-class citizens in traditional Judaism, and perhaps Jesus could offer a full equality.

Philip is from Bethsaida, as you know, which is a mixed city of Jews and pagans, including Greeks, and indeed, 'Philip' is a Greek name. Perhaps it was because of his name that our visitors sought him out and asked whether he would introduce them to Jesus.

Philip was a bit unsure about this, especially so close to the Passover, and therefore he consulted with Andrew. Andrew again was a good choice, because he is another of our band from Bethsaida, and also has a Greek name. More importantly, Andrew was constitutionally incapable of turning anybody away, and promptly bore them off together with Philip to find Jesus.

With his usual gift for being in the right place at the right time, Jesus was teaching in the court of the Gentiles when they found him.

When Andrew told him who the Greeks were, Jesus seemed to consider it most significant.

'The time is come,' was his first remark, which was quite disconcerting to the strangers. It was almost as if he regarded them as ambassadors from the wider world, come to bring him a message that was a call to action.

'The time has come. If the eyes of your hearts are open, you will see God at work, and that within a very few days,' he said.

119

As you know, Jesus was familiar with quite a few aspects of pagan religions, and so he continued in terms that they would understand both from their past roots and from their present hopes.

'Hear the word of truth. Only when the wheat seed dies does the new life spring up,' he said. 'Death leads to resurrection, and the seed is the sign of this.'

A great deal of Western religion is based on the cycles of nature, and especially on the rhythm of the harvest, the deadness of winter and the new life of spring. Many of their stories are about a dying god who comes to life again.

He then added the same idea, but in more Eastern terms.

'If you cling to your life, it will become as nothing. Forget self, and you will live the life of eternity.'

Then Jesus stopped. It was as if he had forgotten the Greeks. His face was troubled, and he seemed to be looking through the crowd around him, through the Temple and its hustle, beyond them to a world that was invisible to the rest of us.

'God save me,' he muttered.

He bent over for a minute, bowed by the weight of whatever was going through his mind, and then shook himself. Not to rid himself of the burden, but to settle it into place. He straightened up again.

'God will save us all,' he said, in a stronger voice, 'and I shall do my part.'

As if to confirm this promise, there was a sudden rumble of thunder in the cloudless sky.

'What was that?' whispered one of our Greek visitors, awed and almost overwhelmed by this brief encounter.

'An angel?' muttered someone in the crowd.

Jesus looked at the Greek, and with an effort smiled though his dark mood to the one who was asking for his teaching.

'Make of it what you will,' he said. 'It was, after all, entirely for your benefit.'

His black mood was passing. Not rejected, but taken into himself and accepted, and he was ready to explain to those who were able to hear it.

'The world's crisis is here,' he said. 'Choose now where you stand. Know that the ways of the world are doomed.

'As for me, I shall be lifted onto a tree. The curse of death will be an exaltation into life. All people can then come to me; can come to God.'

With an encircling wave of his arm he indicated the Greeks and then swept round the rest of his listeners. His gesture was so compelling that I looked up, half-expecting to see the Mount of Olives and the environs of Jerusalem covered with crowds hastening to the death of the son of God.

Even the slowest of his listeners could understand that he was talking of dying, and specifically of crucifixion. A voice came from the crowd of someone who was clearly still wrestling with the question of who Jesus might be.

'But the Messiah will stay for ever,' he said. 'So who can *you* be?'

Jesus reverted to his favourite proverb.

'Light!' he exclaimed, 'Light! Walk while you have light to see by. Choose now, for God's sake and for your own. You can be a child of the light.'

This was the last word that Jesus uttered in public as a free man.

As soon as he had said it he turned to the little knot of Greeks and bowed to them as if indeed they were ambassadors. He flashed a smile upon them, and left them, puzzled as they were and deeply moved, to the care of Andrew.

He left the Temple and went out to Bethany, staying there until his return with the rest of us to share our last meal together.

Chapter 15

Jesus made the move that would finish the meal.
'Let us pray,' he said:

Now, Lover God. Now!
The time has come.
It is the lifting time:
Lift me on high
and I shall lift up you.
I come from you,
Bearing and sharing life of eternity.
Now bring me home with those you've given me.
They know I'm yours.
They've glimpsed your word and works,
Seeking and journeying
With me
And so with you.

Now, Lover God. Now!
Make them beloved too.
I ask for them,
Not for the world at large;
Not for the world of power, self and wealth;
But for these few,
These seeking, struggling few.
And as I come to you,
These few take on the world,
And they must face its hate,
Its fear of truth and love.
Keep them, O Love, keep them in seeking truth.
Keep them, O Closest, keep them in being love.
As you sent me
I send them now,

Fourth Witness

My mark upon their hearts
As you mark me.

Not these alone,
But those they touch and change.
Take them and teach them
So they may share in us.
Let them be one in love, O Lover God,
As I am one with you and you with me.
Let them be one
So that the world may see
The better path of love;
Life of eternity.

Now, Lover God. Now!
I end my prayer to you
Deep in your heart
Where I shall always be.
Make this their place and home,
Lifted, like me, to you.
This is beyond the world,
And yet it came to be

Because of your love;
Your love which sent them me.   Amen.

Chapter 16

The 'Amen' in response to Jesus' prayer was pretty muted. I opened my mouth to shape the word, but nothing passed the lump in my throat. It was clear to us all that Jesus had just made his will, leaving to us all that he was and all that God had given to him.

Both Mary's were weeping in their different ways; Mary of Bethany quite openly and unaffectedly, and Mary of Magdala silently but with the tears glistening clear upon her cheeks. Martha had reached across to her brother, who was sitting at the nearest corner of one of the extra tables, and was gripping his hand. Andrew and Nathaniel similarly had their hands entwined, while on the couch across from them, Peter had drawn his cloak over his face, James was staring down at his hands and Thomas, never one to flinch, was gazing straight at Jesus as he finished.

I felt another change in Jesus, as a tingle ran through his body. He reached for his beaker, drained it of wine, and set it back on the table in the way one does when it is time to go. He stood. His smile swept all of us, long and slow, again treasuring and bringing to mind our own special encounters with him. I thought of our moments with him as he washed our feet. Was that only a few hours ago? Maybe, in the world's time, but we had lived far more in that Upper Room in the life of eternity. Not the easy option it had sometimes seemed when Jesus first began explaining it to us.

With one of his typical encircling gestures he invited us all to follow him as he made for the door. Joseph opened it and slipped out ahead - he would not wish to be seen with us in the open street. The oblong of blackness he left reminded me of the darkness that had swallowed Judas, and into which Jesus was now striding. And then I was out through the door myself, and realised that it was only black by contrast, as the Passover moon was shining bright and high in the sky to the south-east of us.

Jesus led us from the upper city down the steps to the old lower city and out through the gate by the Pool of Siloam. We then turned north to walk up the Kidron Valley towards the garden at the foot of the Mount of Olives. It was a garden where we had often met on our way to or from Bethany.

The Kidron is not a pleasant valley. It was quiet enough that night, perhaps too quiet, but I could not help thinking that the next day it would be flowing with the blood of the Passover sacrifices, all of which was washed into the valley from the Temple looming up high on our left. The stream, a winter one, had dried up weeks before. Over on our right, spectral in the moonlight, were the rock-hewn tombs of the rich of a hundred years ago, carved into fantastical shapes and sightless black caves.

I was surprised that Jesus had brought the women with him (a glance at Martha had been enough for all of them to desert the clearing and the washing up) and then I realised that this was again to think as the world thinks. Jesus had just shared his testament with us all equally, and that, in his book, would include the danger and risks no less than the gifts and benefits of the life of eternity. I remembered he had also promised our safety, although I wondered how he could guarantee that. Certainly, no-one wanted to be left behind on this night of nights.

Lost in my own thoughts, we were nearly at the garden before I realised that no-one else was talking either. Peter was walking, marching almost, close to Jesus, and his right hand was under his cloak, no doubt grasping the hilt of his ceremonial dagger. Thomas, too, was walking towards the front, as if almost eager to embrace the outcome he had predicted. Nathaniel's lips were moving silently in the recitation of a psalm; probably one for deliverance from enemies.

We entered the garden and sat down in small groups. We could all see one another sharply black and white in the moonlight, with Jesus standing in the middle. He was clearly waiting. I went to stand next to him, and he glanced swiftly at me, and then back at the gate. I remembered his words to Judas, 'Do it. Do it now. Get it over.' Jesus nodded as if in confirmation of my guess.

Almost immediately we could see a considerable crowd begin to emerge through the gate just to the south of the Temple platform, and begin to make their way up the valley towards us. They were carrying torches and lanterns, which cast no light at all in the bright moonlight, but rather seemed to be the necessary props and adjuncts for a deed of darkness. There was the glint of bronze and copper, and we realised that soldiers were with them. Had we wished to run, there was time and enough, for it was not a stealthy or well-managed affair. They must have been told that Jesus would not seek to escape.

We stood, waiting in the garden.

Then, as the crowd neared, Jesus strode out of the garden to meet them. As always in these moments of confrontation, he seemed to know exactly who he was and what he should do next. They shuffled to a halt a few yards away from where Jesus stood, his cloak thrown back from his face, and his features, among the best known in Jerusalem, clearly visible.

'Who are you searching for that matters so much?' (I remembered his first words to Andrew and me; still at this stage Jesus was offering choices, even to this band of state thugs.)

126

'Jesus, the Nazarene,' came the reply, from somewhere near the middle of the crowd.

'I am.'

No mistaking this, and those at the front, who in the main were Jewish Temple police, sank to their knees, or even prostrated themselves, leaving the Romans who were with them looking distinctly uneasy at the turn of events. Despite all that had been said in the Upper Room, I wondered for a moment if Jesus was going to pull off another of his escapes.

Right at the front, alone on his feet and sticking out like the last sheaf in a harvested field, was Judas.

Looking straight at Judas, Jesus repeated his challenge.

'Who are you searching for that matters so much?'

The Roman officer came forward, and it was significant that he was a senior officer; the Romans were clearly deeply concerned about the whole business. One wondered what had been said to Pilate, the Roman governor, to arrange this coup.

'We seek Jesus the Nazarene,' he said. He summoned the courage to look Jesus in the eye, waiting for him to give himself up.

Jesus spoke to the officer. 'Then if I am he whom you seek, let these others alone. You have no orders about them.'

The officer nodded, and Jesus stepped towards him, half turning as he did so to bid farewell to us. This was more than Peter could take. No doubt the charges of desertion were still ringing in his head, and with them the frustration of the whole half-understood evening in the Upper Room. He lunged forward, past the officer (who had shown respect for Jesus, and in any case was foreign) and lashed out at the first person he came to in the crowd. He had drawn his dagger as he went, and he slashed back-handed at the man, nicking his ear and drawing copious blood. I suspect that the back-hand blow was Peter trying to dispose of an obstacle on his way to Judas, but it was the only blow struck.

Jesus was there in an instant, in front of Peter and compelling his obedience. 'Put that silly dagger away, Peter.

This is God's work. Will you stop me from doing it?'

The Roman officer, seeing Jesus' action, had made a sign to his own troops, and half-unsheathed swords (twice as long and ten times as heavy as Peter's) slid back into their sheaths.

Almost apologetically, the officer produced a leather thong and bound it round Jesus' unresisting wrists. He then put his hand on Jesus' shoulder, and urged him towards the Temple police. It was clearly to be their arrest.

They set off with him back down the valley, rather than continuing up to the Antonia fortress where the Romans were barracked, and this again indicated that he was being taken to one of the senior Temple officials, maybe the high priest himself, and not to the Roman governor.

We were left standing stricken in the moonlight. I found that I was next to Peter, my hand clamped firmly round his sword-arm, and with Mary of Magdala holding him on the other side. The other women had retreated into the garden, with Andrew hovering protectively around them. Understandable, as soldiers might have had much less respect for women abroad at night than did Jesus. Others of the band were standing in twos and threes, clearly unable to comprehend what had just happened, despite Jesus' forewarnings of the last few hours. Everyone felt very much at risk. If Jesus was taken, was it not a matter of time before they came for us? And it would not be the upright and honourable Roman officer, but gangs and bounty hunters only too ready to swing with the tide.

Bethany lay invitingly over the hill, less than forty minutes away on a cool bright night, and that's where most of the leaderless remains of our band went, to the home of Martha and her brother and sister.

There were exceptions. Mary of Magdala said nothing, but was plainly not going to leave Jerusalem at this time, and Peter was all for following Jesus and his captors. I knew that nothing would dissuade him from this; he already felt badly enough about what he had done, and Jesus' prophecy of his desertion was still ringing in his head. I too wanted to follow, telling myself that Peter needed a minder, now more than ever. In truth I just wanted to get back as close to Jesus as I could. He'd been gone less than five minutes, but already I felt more lonely and desolate than ever in my whole life. Indeed, he, his closeness to God, his life of eternity, *were* my whole life, and this struck home with a dreadful clarity as I watched the captor band receding down the valley.

So we followed, Peter and Mary and I, at a distance, and desperately hoping that no-one would look back and see us. At least, I was hoping none of them would see Peter, who could hardly be popular with them at this moment.

We entered Jerusalem by the same gate we had left through such a short time ago, and saw that the captors were heading up the steps towards the upper city; again, the same steps we had so recently descended. Following, we saw them turn into one of the high priest's houses, about two thirds of the way up; one of the several houses from which the high-priestly aristocracy ran our affairs, and one with which I was familiar. Truth be told, my family had served at times in all of them.

Mary left us here, with a few words about Jesus' mother and her need to know what was happening; the first time she had spoken since we began our return journey. She disappeared further up the hill in search of Jesus' family.

The door to the house was standing open, with a portress on duty. Like the gates of the city itself, nothing official was shut this night, but that was because of all the comings and goings surrounding the Passover, which was to begin tomorrow. No! Later that day, I realised.

I recognised the young lady at the door, and she certainly knew me, because she smiled and nodded as I walked past.

I was standing in the courtyard, which was full of the Temple police that officially had captured Jesus, and beyond them I could see the smaller courtyard used by senior priests to hear petitions and deal with administrative matters. This was where Jesus was, standing before a table with officials sitting behind it. Through the crowd I caught a glimpse of the man seated at the centre, and as I saw his face, realised that it was none other than Annas, father-in-law of our high priest Caiaphas. Annas had himself been high priest, and had succeeded, when the Romans retired him, in keeping the office in his family. Annas was not good news for Jesus, and I remember thinking about his son-in-law's remark that it was wise to let one man die for the sake of the rest of us. Annas held the same pragmatic view of politics, and would not think twice about arranging Jesus' execution if it meant a peaceful Passover.

I was distracted from my thoughts by a disturbance behind me. The portress was not for letting Peter in, and Peter was not for being kept out. I turned and ran back to the door. Peter had already drawn enough attention to himself that night, and could hardly be popular with the high priest's staff at this moment in time.

'He's with me,' I said to the young lady.

'Oh, that's all right then,' she replied. 'Another one of his disciples?' This with a nod towards the inner courtyard.

'I am not,' growled Peter. He had his cloak over his head, and would not look at me. I was taken by surprise by his denial, and could only assume that he had taken to heart my remarks about keeping a low profile. I had been impressing on him the way with the need for no more swordplay or indeed any disturbance that could only make things worse for Jesus. Trust Peter to take it further than I had meant.

The crowd inside seemed good-natured enough, if a bit loud and happy in the relief of a dangerous mission safely accomplished. I was realising how frightened the Temple police had become of arresting Jesus in the light of their earlier attempts. I felt it was safe to leave Peter there, especially in his present mood, warming himself by a new-kindled charcoal fire, while I pushed my way through to the inner part of the courtyard.

Annas glanced indifferently at me as I went to stand as near Jesus as I could. Remembering his words in the Upper Room, I had half an idea that I could stand beside him as the 'prisoner's friend' in his hour of need. But Jesus was managing fine on his own.

It transpired that Annas was interrogating Jesus about his teaching and specifically about what he had been saying to us, his followers, in private.

'I have taught you all openly and directly,' was Jesus' retort. 'I have taught in the synagogues and in the Temple, which are open to all. I have no 'secret' teaching as if the things of God were for a chosen few. You must accept this, or mount a trial and call witnesses.'

What Jesus said was entirely true, and within his rights. Annas was sailing dangerously close to the wind in terms of our law, and could, in theory at least, find himself in the role of the accused if he did not accept Jesus' word or prove the contrary. However Jesus' reply did not please one of the Temple guards standing there, for he turned and struck Jesus a hard open-handed slap across the face.

'That's no way to talk to a high priest,' he snarled.

There was blood in the corner of Jesus' mouth, and his eyes flashed almost in contempt at someone who would strike a bound man. He reiterated his right to a trial.

'If I speak amiss, it is for you to prove it,' he said, 'and if I speak the truth then why resort to violence?'

Annas lifted a weary hand from the table, palm down and fingers towards the policeman.

'Enough,' he said. 'This gets us nowhere. Take him to Caiaphas.'

I tried to follow, but was refused leave by Annas, while

Jesus was taken to another part of the house. It was clear that neither Annas nor his son-in-law were going to risk a trial. As I have told you, this ploy had failed on several occasions. These were private questionings, and while they might be looking for things to use against Jesus, it seemed that the purpose was much more for the high priests, current and retired, to reassure themselves that Jesus was not what he claimed to be. The authorities had understood the thrust of Jesus' teaching better than most, and I suspect that there was still a corner in each of these supremely practical men that wondered if he might be telling the truth. Time, experience and the continual need to be politically adept had rendered them both pragmatists, and deeply cynical about other people, but still they were priests, and they too, in a curious way, were concerned for the things of God.

I took comfort from the fact that clearly no trial was intended, because I knew they would not dream of having Jesus killed without one, and began to wonder if they had simply decided to keep him out of the way for the duration of the feast. On the other hand, both Nicodemus and Joseph had warned us that the talk in the Council was of death.

Suddenly I remembered the very senior Roman officer at the garden, out of place in this affair. Like a lead weight in the pit of my stomach it occurred to me that they were going to get the Romans to execute Jesus. Eerily, as this thought hit me, the cock crew.

I returned to the outer part of the courtyard to look for Peter. He was gone, and I soon got the story from those around the fire. It turned out I was not the only one to hear the cock.

While Annas had been questioning Jesus, Peter had been trying to keep to his unaccustomed role of the low profile. It was a lost cause, however. Not only had he been introduced into the house by me, a known associate of Jesus, but far too many had seen his swordplay outside the garden. He had soon been challenged again to admit that he was another follower of Jesus. Again he denied it in the same words I had heard him use to the maid at the door, which curiously are an exact negative of Jesus' challenging 'I am'.

The crowd knew better, however, and asked someone who had been close to the action; indeed related to the man whose ear Peter nicked, and who name turned out to be Malchus. (The story had grown in the telling, and Peter was now credited with cutting Malchus' ear off.)

Malchus' relative said directly to Peter, 'I saw you. I'm sure it was you in the garden.'

On his third denial, the cock crew. This had proved too much for Peter. He had gone.

I remembered how insistent I had been that he say nothing to provoke anyone. Was I entirely innocent in these denials by Peter? I realised that I had played my part, a forgiven part, but still a part, as I had in the betrayal by Judas.

The odd thing was that the crowd in the courtyard would have done nothing to Peter if he had admitted who he was. The action was over from their point of view, as I discovered in my own reception by them. Peter had made his choice and acted not on the reality of the situation, but in terms of his own fears and guilt. He was not the only one to do so that day.

Chapter 17

They *were* going to get the Romans to execute Jesus.

After an uneasy few hours in the courtyard, when a few of the police tried to sleep, but without much success, a semi-procession emerged from Caiaphas' end of the yard. It was first light. Caiaphas was in the lead, and Jesus was at the centre. It was plain that none of them had slept either.

Annas and some of his lawyers joined them, and there was a brief and muted discussion. A police chief rounded up some of the Temple police to form an escort.

I walked across to them and managed to catch Annas' eye, and with a weary twitch of his eyebrow he gave me permission to accompany them. Everything that Annas did these days had the sign of intense weariness about it, as if he had seen everything and everything had disappointed him. If ever there was anybody in need of Jesus' life of eternity, it was Annas.

We set off through the misty streets up the hill and westwards towards Herod's great fortress-palace, where we knew Pilate, the Roman governor, to be staying for the duration of the feast. Although I was allowed to accompany them, the guards would not let me near Jesus, and so the most I could do was catch his eye and smile a hollow smile of encouragement. He smiled back a smile of much more genuine encouragement, and I could almost hear his voice in my head.

'Ah, my fourth witness! Watch and take note, Beloved.'

When we arrived at the palace, we stopped outside at the stone platform built by the Herods for their appearances in public. The Romans used it for the same purpose, when staying in Jerusalem. Technically they were guests of the Herod family, but in practice the 'prætorium', the Roman seat of government, moved there with them.

We were clearly expected, for the official judgment chair was already set out on the dais, placed between two doors that led, as I discovered, into Pilate's office.

We were expected in another sense, too, which made even clearer the fact that there had been preliminary discussions between Pilate and Caiaphas concerning Jesus and his arrest, and explained the presence of the legionaries the night before. For as we arrived, Pilate himself came out to meet us. It was no surprise to find him up and about. Romans, especially those in high office, pride themselves on having their routine paperwork done by sunrise.

Pilate was not seeking to do Caiaphas and Annas any special courtesy by coming out to them. It had been pre-arranged so that the high priest, with his special responsibilities in the coming feast, should not contract ritual impurity by actually setting foot on the prætorium. (It is not that non-Jews are impure in themselves, but that they may have contracted impurity by going too close to a corpse or lying with a menstruating woman - things that soldiers are notoriously prone to do. It was typical of all that Jesus disliked about legal observances that this nicety should figure as a thing of significance when the heart of the Law itself was effectively on trial.) As events unfolded that morning, I realised that actually Pilate was pleased to have the high priests down at the foot of the tribunal, putting them in the position of supplicants rather than co-judges.

Pilate sat in the judgment seat and looked down at us, his gaze lingering on Jesus, the cause of all this bother, and then moving on to Caiaphas.

'What charge do you bring against this man?' he asked in the traditional formula.

This clearly took the high priests by surprise. They must

have been expecting an instant condemnation, a mere formality, and instead Pilate obviously intended a full trial by Roman rules.

Caiaphas recovered swiftly, and tried to carry it off with a high hand and in his best declamatory voice.

'If this fellow were not a persistent felon, we should not be handing him over to you,' he said.

This cut no ice with Pilate, who immediately responded, 'Judge him by your own law, then.' If they had made this much fuss about Jesus already, 'persistent felon' was scarcely a sufficient charge.

'We cannot carry out the death penalty,' was the response.

This was true, but a bit disingenuous. It was legally the case that for the last twenty-four years or so, under Roman rule, the so-called 'right of the sword' had been withheld from the Temple authorities, but the Romans were known to turn a blind eye to stonings carried out under our Law, and indeed themselves enforced these in the case of non-Jews crossing the barrier of the Temple. It was clear, as Jesus had foretold, that the religious leadership was set on him being crucified, not stoned, as crucifixion would place him under God's curse. This, they thought, would be an end to all Jesus' claims of a special relationship with God.

Pilate was to some extent playing with the local leadership. He had suffered quite a bit from Jewish religious sensibilities, and made some dangerous mistakes. He had no love for the religious authorities, and was out to get a bit of his own back.

Having wrong-footed Caiaphas in this initial exchange, Pilate settled down to the case in hand. He beckoned Jesus to go into the inner chamber with him. I stepped across onto the prætorium, and apart from finding a burly legionary instantly beside me and watching my every move, I was allowed to follow.

Inside, Pilate seated himself beside a low table upon which

papers and book-rolls were neatly stacked, and gestured Jesus to stand in front of him, again with a legionary by his side. I stood just inside the doorway, unobtrusively in the shadows. The conversation was, of course, in Greek, the common language of a large part of the world, though neither Jesus nor Pilate spoke it as their first tongue.

'Are you the King of the Jews?' asked Pilate. So that's what he had been told; that Jesus was another of these bandit freedom fighters with an imagined mandate from God. Jesus recognised it instantly.

'Now who put that into your head?' he wondered, and not at all in the tone of voice that Pilate was accustomed to in those who appeared before him. You could see Pilate pause and stare hard at Jesus, instantly revising his opinion of the case.

'It's hardly a Roman thought,' said Pilate, and he tapped a paper beside him on the table. 'You have been handed over to me by your own people who think these things. Now tell me straight, what have you been up to?'

Jesus could not be expected to explain his whole history of confrontation with the authorities in such a way that Pilate would understand, and so he reverted to Pilate's first question, hoping that this would provide an adequate answer to the second, too.

'I'm not a king in any sense that either you or the world would mean. I have kingship in a religious dimension that both lies at the heart of this world and is nothing to do with it at all.'

Puzzlement was setting in on Pilate's face, and so Jesus tried a more direct argument.

'If I were a king in your meaning, I too would have 'Temple police', there would have been a fight, and I would not have been surrendered to the religious authorities.'

This made more sense to Pilate, and so he put the question again, based on Jesus' admission.

'Ah, then you are a king?'

'Yes,' said Jesus, 'although the word comes more naturally from your lips than from mine. I am sovereign in the life of eternity, and my whole purpose and reason for existence in this world is to share this truth. Anyone who cares for truth will recognise this by what I am and say.'

Cynicism and a sneaking respect struggled for a moment together on Pilate's face. Then world-weariness entered his eyes, almost as if to say, 'You won't find any truth in the political games of this court or this country. If you place your hope in truth, it's doomed here.' He put his thoughts into two words.

'Truth?... Hah!'

And with that he rose and went outside again to confront Jesus' accusers.

Standing where I was, I could see as well as hear Pilate's next encounter, this time with the high priests and the lawyers.

'I find him innocent,' Pilate declared. He paused to enjoy the consternation that he was causing among our leaders. This was not at all how they had planned it. They could hardly revert to stoning Jesus now, and if Pilate wouldn't crucify him then he might escape after all.

Then Pilate offered everyone a way out with dignity.

'Your feast is a feast of freedom,' he said, 'And you mark it with the release of prisoners. I have often done the same for you. Will you accept this so-called King of the Jews?'

There was a hasty consultation between Caiaphas and his senior advisors. Annas was standing a little to one side, watching with hooded eyes. They came to an agreement, and one of the senior clergy called out their answer. Shouting up to Pilate had become a little too demeaning for Caiaphas himself.

'Not this fellow. We choose Barabbas.'

This in turn caught Pilate by surprise. He was in a cleft stick, for Barabbas was indeed what they had tried to make

Jesus out to be; a bandit and a fanatic. The governor could hardly refuse when the charges were so similar.

He turned on his heel and came inside again. He was white about the lips, and anger was flashing in his eyes. He hardly glanced at Jesus as he said in a hard level voice, 'Scourge him.'

My legionary suddenly had my upper arm in a vice-like grip, and he was looking down at me warningly as they led Jesus down some stairs at the back of the hall. I could hear and see nothing but felt it all the same. The time seemed hardly to move at all.

Meanwhile, Pilate was pacing up and down the room. I realised that Jesus meant very little to him. All this was a power game that he was playing with Caiaphas and our leaders. He had tried to get Jesus off, and might try again, settling for a scourging rather than crucifixion, but guilt and innocence were very secondary considerations to Pilate.

Then they brought Jesus back. They had been gone some time, and plainly had been making sport of him as well as administering the beating. An upright man had walked with them down the stair; it was a mangled and limping Jesus that staggered back up, half supported by the soldiers.

They had dressed him in a mockery of an imperial purple cloak, and a mock crown of acanthus thorns was jammed onto his head, the spikes sticking up and out in a horrible parody of the divine crowns which we see on foreign coins. Not only his back, but his face was bleeding, puffy and discoloured. He had clearly been subject to taunting and blows as well as the scourging. The soldiers had taken up the charge of 'kingship' and made a cruel game of it.

Pilate surveyed his handiwork and then said, 'Hold him here, just inside the door.'

I looked in horror at my friend, and his eyes in his broken face glinted back at me pain-filled. And yet within the pain itself there was still Jesus' spirit, entire and as yet unassailed, and almost a message of hope. The legionary gripped me again, warningly, and I said nothing.

Pilate was out on the dais again, his back to us, but I could still hear the anger and contempt in his voice as he looked down at the group of religious leaders. They must have wondered what was coming, and what had taken so long.

'Look!' said Pilate. 'I still find him innocent. He is not what you say. See for yourselves!'

With that he gestured to the soldiers who stepped forward through the door and into the sunlight with Jesus between them in all his mock glory. Curiously, even in that twisted and battered form, he did indeed look like a king; not one of power and wealth and manipulation, but, as he had claimed to Pilate, sovereign in the life of eternity.

'Look well!' said Pilate. 'This is the man.'

Whatever Pilate had intended by his mock epiphany of Jesus, he had underestimated the intransigence of his audience.

'Crucify him' called out Caiaphas, and his guards and lawyers took up the call, 'Crucify!'

'Oh, do it yourselves,' Pilate snapped back. 'You can see he's no king. He's plainly innocent.'

Pilate had lost all patience at this point, and had left an opening for Caiaphas to construe his words as offering back to the local authorities the 'right of the sword'. Caiaphas, however, intent on his pursuit of Jesus, missed this opportunity, and desperate that Jesus should be crucified, now, today, came out with the real charge that he had against Jesus. He had clearly not meant to share this with the governor, no doubt following previous failures to get Pilate to take our beliefs seriously.

'He *must* die. He claims to be God's own son. In our law that is unforgivable and *must* be punished by death.'

That stopped Pilate dead in his tracks. He froze, then wheeled on his heel and with a swirl of his cloak virtually fled back into the inner office, waving an arm to have Jesus brought back inside. As he passed me I could see fear in his face. He was the last man I would have expected to pay any attention to the things of God, but clearly something, Jesus himself perhaps, had moved him. Caiaphas' words had proved most unwelcome to him.

Not even pausing to sit down, Pilate confronted the bleeding Jesus.

'Just where are you from?' he demanded. 'In all truth, where are you coming from?'

Jesus said nothing, his silence underlining Pilate's own unexpected desire for 'truth'. For a moment each looked steadily at the other. Pilate was the first to break.

'Silent? Why? The power is mine to release you. Equally, the power is mine to crucify you.'

Even as he said this, rehearsing his powers, there was a note of uncertainty in his voice, which Jesus picked up and mirrored back to him.

'Your power over me is not yours, it is given you for a season from the world of eternity. In truth you are powerless in the grip of your own fears. This will lead you to do wrong, but greater still is the wrong of those who have set us both in this position.'

Something in Jesus' words may have touched a chord in Pilate's cynical and power-serving heart, for he went out a third time to demand Jesus' release. But Annas and Caiaphas had not been idle. They had seen the effect of the phrase 'son of God' on Pilate, and decided to get him back onto the kingship charge, this time with a new argument.

'If you release this fellow, with his claims, you are hardly championing your master, Cæsar; you who bear the title 'Cæsar's friend'. Anyone claiming kingship, anyone at all, is challenging Cæsar.'

They had indeed played to Pilate's fears. An adverse report to Tiberius would bring out various other troubles that Pilate had had, and he could ill afford an inquiry. Tiberius Cæsar himself, semi-recluse on the island of Capri, was of a suspicious and unforgiving nature, as Pilate knew well.

At that point Caiaphas had won, and Pilate deeply resented it. He determined to humiliate Caiaphas as Caiaphas had him. If Caiaphas had struck at Pilate's political centre, then Pilate would strike at Caiaphas' religion. Jesus had ceased to matter except as a pawn in the game.

Pilate called Jesus out to stand beside him and sat down on the judgment seat.

The time was close to noon on the preparation day for the Passover of that year. The place was Herod's platform, known in Greek as the 'Stone Pavement' and in Aramaic as the 'Lifted Ground'.

'Look then, at your king,' said Pilate to the priests, stressing the word 'king'.

'Take him away! Crucify him!' they screamed back at him, stung by Pilate's apparent insistence that in the light of their last claim, Jesus was indeed a king.

'Crucify your king?' sneered Pilate, although he was still white with anger. Again, the stress on the title.

There was a short pause, and then Caiaphas' voice could be heard, determined to drive home the clincher.

'He is *not* our king. Our only king is Cæsar!'

Pilate sat back in the judgment chair. He had got what he wanted. Caiaphas, the chief priest, had publicly put Cæsar, an earthly ruler, before God as our king. Pilate had made Caiaphas, however unintentionally, deny his God and betray his religion.

With a wave of his arm, and not even looking over his shoulder at Jesus, Pilate indicated that the soldiers should take him away and crucify him.

Chapter 18

We set out immediately, going northward and then turning eastward along the wall to the Garden Gate, and out of the city. Jesus was made to carry his own cross-piece, as was the custom; an extra torture as it weighed down on his lacerated back. But it seemed as if he accepted, indeed welcomed, the task as his own choice, and not an imposition dictated by others. We were heading for a small outcrop of rock in the old quarry just outside the city, and close to the main road. It was known as 'the place of the skull', because of its shape, or 'Golgotha' in Aramaic.

Jesus was stripped and laid on the cross-piece, and with his arms stretched out, nails were driven through his wrists. The soldiers knew their business, and were cruelly efficient. Almost immediately he was hauled up onto the waiting upright, and the cross-piece slotted into place. His legs were twisted onto the upright, and another nail driven through both ankles. Although pain clouded his battered face, still crowned with the thorny circlet, and he seemed close to fainting, not a sound did he make throughout the torture.

Two terrorists were to be crucified at the same time, no doubt colleagues of Barabbas, and they soon followed Jesus on the stakes either side of him.

To each cross was added a placard with the alleged crime for which they died, and we discovered that Pilate had by no means finished his taunting of the high priests. The placard he had caused to be placed over Jesus read 'Jesus the Nazarene, the King of the Jews'. It was written in three languages, Aramaic, Latin and Greek, so that all could read it. Pilate was doing much more with this placard than giving the charge against Jesus; he seemed both to be asserting that Jesus was truly a king, and would not be on the cross for anything less, and also he was declaring it to all the world, whatever their language and nationality.

We heard later that Caiaphas had indeed objected to this, trying to get it changed to 'This fellow claimed to be King of the Jews', but Pilate would have none of it. He had been landed with the responsibility for executing Jesus, and maintained his right to do it his way. He told the religious authorities, 'I wrote it; it stays written.'

The four soldiers settled down at the foot of the three crosses to await the deaths of the victims. One of their perks for this unpleasant task was to share out the victims' belongings, and so they proceeded to make four piles, which was fine until they came to Jesus' long under-robe. Despite the mauling it had received in the last few hours, and the blood that stained it liberally, they recognised that it was a fine garment. Indeed, it had been woven as a single piece throughout, and had been a gift to Jesus from Martha. Martha had woven vestments for Temple priests in her time, and this was of that quality.

The legionaries decided to roll dice for it, instead of sharing it, and so that is what they did.

This may not appear significant to you, the reader, but to those of us who know the Bible, it seems very important, as one of our psalms predicts that this is what will happen to God's special chosen servant.

Quite a few moments in the next two hours fell into that category, and it was very noticeable, indeed eerie, for those of us who carry vast chunks of scripture around in our heads. It seemed unmistakable that God had prepared for centuries for this moment.

I was joined at the foot of Jesus' cross by Mary of Magdala. She had found Jesus' family, and been able both to keep abreast of events, and also to let the family know what was happening. Jesus' brothers had made themselves scarce (being related to Jesus could be bad news, just now), but Mary had brought some of the women of the family with her. Jesus' mother was there, and his aunt, and yet another Mary, the wife of a certain Clopas.

Jesus seemed to be in a faint, but when the women drew near he opened his eyes, and managed a pain-filled smile. He saw his mother standing next to me, and almost cheekily, in tones reminiscent of the way he had talked to her at the wedding in Cana (was that only two years ago?) he spoke to her.

'Woman, treat him as your son.' This with the faintest of nods towards me.

And then to me, 'Beloved, treat her as a mother.'

He clearly meant much more than that I should look after her, as she had other sons of her own, but from that moment we had a special relationship, and I took her to my heart, as she did me. It became a relationship that transcended family, and had about it the closeness that Jesus had prayed for among his followers in the Upper Room.

It was a long, long two hours there under the baking sun. Jesus kept drifting in and out of a pain-wracked consciousness, and was clearly dying quite quickly, as these hideous things go. At the foot of the cross, we were holding each other, and gazing up at the stark silhouette against the sky.

We were in a bubble of comparative quiet, as all around us the vast busyness of the Passover preparation was taking place. The area where we were was being avoided by the Passover crowds, who flowed round us just to the north and the south. This was not only because of the curse upon all crucifixions, but also because we were very close to a series of tombs in a small garden, and they carried their own ritual impurity that would prevent one sharing in tonight's feast.

I gazed up at Jesus, lifted up as he had said, 'exalted' in the grim gallows humour of the time, on his hideous parody of a

145

throne, and with Pilate's title of kingship over his head. I was aware that he was dying at the same time as the Passover lambs were being slaughtered in the Temple behind and beyond his cross, and I could see the smoke of sacrifice drifting up and across the sky. Suddenly there came back to me a picture of John the Baptist, standing with his prophet's staff pointing at Jesus and saying, 'Not a king; a lamb.' John had been half right, for indeed, at this extremity of the world, Jesus was both.

Jesus' eyes flickered open and he looked down at me, and I could hear in my head the thought, 'Well done, Beloved. There's my fourth witness.'

The soldiers were kind to us; as kind as their grim duty permitted. They offered to share their food with us, and their cheap wine. We could take nothing, although in a half-hearted way we each urged the other to eat, but again Jesus opened his eyes and looking down at the soldiers said, 'I'm thirsty.' His face had changed and a pallor was in his cheeks, and one of the soldiers whispered encouragingly to his mother, 'Not long, now.'

The soldier tied a sponge to his lance, soaked it in the wine, and pressed it against Jesus' mouth, so that he could drink. It seemed to give Jesus some last flicker of strength, for he lifted his head quite deliberately and looked skywards.

'It is achieved!' he called, his words ringing across the valley.

Then slowly, and with full control, he bowed his head and gave away his life.

Thus far time had gone very slowly, in fact we hardly seemed to be in time at all, but from now on things began to happen with bewildering rapidity, one after the other.

A messenger arrived from Pilate to say that death had to be hastened, as he wanted the bodies off the crosses before sunset. This was as a result of a further petition from the high priests, who did not want the bodies still hanging there when the Sabbath, a special Sabbath as it was also Passover, began. (We count our days as running from sunset to sunset.)

One of the legionaries fetched a large mallet from their macabre toolkit, and used it to smash the legs of the two crucified either side of Jesus. This sounds, and is, horrible, but it brings on a rapid death, as the victim is no longer able to hitch himself up to allow his lungs to fill, and he suffocates rapidly.

When they came to Jesus, however, the leader of the four, who had given the wine, stopped them.

'He's dead already,' he said, and to prove his point prodded Jesus with his spear. The prod was a vigorous one, and the spear sharp. It entered Jesus' side, and to our amazement both blood and water flowed out.

This sounds incredible, but it is true. I was there and I saw it, and I am witness to it. I tell you about it because it may help you too in your journey into life.

This whole incident has special significance for those of us who know the Bible, as it fits with what is written about the Passover victim and about God's dealings with us as our Lover. It all made real for us the knowledge that God was at work here in the death of Jesus. Jesus had not been cursed by the death he died, rather the reverse. Jesus' willing death was, in a curious way, a triumph over the ways of this world and the worst it can do, for death itself is a part of life - the life of eternity.

Almost immediately, yet another messenger arrived from Pilate to say that the body of Jesus was not to be disposed of, but that the governor had granted it to two members of the Jewish Council. In his wake came Joseph of Arimathæa carrying grave clothes and oil, and Nicodemus with a vast sack of myrrh and aloes. It seems that both of them had laid aside their fear of their fellow council members. Interesting that it was Jesus' apparent *defeat* that should bring them out into the open. By touching a body, they were also rendering themselves ritually impure, and therefore would be cut off from the Passover celebrations - a huge sacrifice for people like Joseph and Nicodemus.

Nicodemus had brought a tremendous amount of spices, at least seventy-five pounds, I would have thought, judging by the laboured way he was carrying it up the knoll. He was a member of the party of reform, of course, and so was meticulous in the matter of treating Jesus' body properly, and Joseph too knew what to do.

With the help of two of the legionaries they un-nailed Jesus from the cross, and lowered his body onto the waiting cloths. They then anointed him with the spices mixed with the oil, and wrapped the body together with the spices in the cloths.

Sunset was close at hand, and there was a need for haste, but Joseph had it planned.

He had been talking with the owner of one of the graves in the garden right next to the Place of the Skull. This was a new tomb, as yet unused, and Joseph had obtained permission to lay Jesus' body there. We carried the torn and mistreated corpse down off the knoll and laid it in the tomb.

As we closed the tomb, the sun set. The Passover had begun.

Chapter 19

I remember very little of that Passover Sabbath, which we did not even attempt to celebrate, and which we passed in a dull black despair.

Mary and I had returned to our base in Jerusalem; actually one of my father's houses, and I had taken Jesus' mother home with me, as she felt unequal to returning to her family and their Passover feast. Her sister and Mary of Clopas had gone to explain this to their relatives. We had found Peter at our house, but he was silent and withdrawn, spending his time alone in our upper room. Of the rest we saw nothing that day.

It was the following day that everything began to happen. If, as I tell you what happened, it seems to have a dream-like quality, then that indeed is how it was. Not that we dreamed a moment of it. All, all was incredibly real and is etched as deeply and as fresh in our memories as if it were happening now. Moments of deep truth and deep change have this strange quality about them, when the life of eternity bursts through and spills out into the humdrum world.

Mary of Magdala had not been able to sleep, and could no longer stay still after the enforced idleness of the Sabbath. She was up and dressed while it was still dark, and leaving the city by means of the Garden Gate, she returned to where we had buried Jesus in the rush of Friday evening. Although Mary was a resourceful and practical woman, well able to take care of herself, this was nevertheless a brave thing to do, alone and in the aftermath of a feast.

As she approached the tomb, she could make out in the brightening dawn that the stone had been removed from the entrance to the tomb. It was totally still and silent, and *empty*. Mary had no need to look inside, she *knew* at that moment that it was empty. Emptiness seemed to stream out from it and surround and fill her. It was this that drove her from the tomb.

She turned and fled. At first she simply picked up her skirts and ran, but the direction she happened to take was back to the city, and as she came through the gate, her flight became more purposeful. Within minutes she was back at the house, calling up to Peter and myself on the roof.

'He's gone!' she was shouting. 'They've taken him! He's not in the tomb, and who knows where they've put him!'

We were up in an instant; we had been able to sleep no more than had Mary. We half ran, half fell down the steps, cannoning off each other in our haste, and headed for the tomb with Mary behind us. Peter and I ran as fast as we could, and side by side. Through the gate and towards the tomb. As we neared it, Peter hesitated and dropped behind. I realised that he did not know exactly where it was, and was waiting for me to show him the way.

I got there first, and bent down to look inside, although I could already feel, as Mary had, that it was empty. I could see a flash of white; presumably the grave clothes, but that was all.

Peter arrived, breathing hard, but whether that was from the running or from some deeper reason, I could not tell. He bent double and eased himself into the tomb, and then stood to one side so that he was not blocking the strengthening daylight. Beside him was the slab where we had laid Jesus, and lying on it the grave clothes, but with the headpiece still wound round and round itself and lying separately. They looked curiously undisturbed, except for the fact that there was clearly no body.

I joined Peter inside, gazing down at the cloths on the otherwise empty shelf. This was not the work of grave robbers, still less of the authorities. Who would unwrap a body before stealing it? Who would re-position the grave-clothes afterwards? There was something of God about this, I knew. I still didn't understand, although a wider knowledge of the Bible might have given me the necessary clue, but I began to believe that we were again in the presence of the life of eternity. It was not something I could put my finger on, certainly not something I could articulate enough to share with Mary and Peter, but it was there.

Mary stayed outside the tomb after we left. We had had a good look round, but there was nothing to see, and I was not expecting anything, and so eventually we returned back to the house.

Mary was weeping. It was more than the disappearance of the body; it was the culmination of the last three days. She had been resourceful in the garden on Thursday, and busy with communicating with Jesus' family. She had been incredibly brave on Friday, supporting Jesus, and all of us, through his final hours. She had been quietly caring for us all on Saturday. Now it all swept over her and she was crying her heart out in front of the tomb.

As she wept, she crouched down to look into the tomb.

What she saw was not what Peter and I had seen. The empty slab with the cloths was still there, but Mary saw two strangers, sitting at either end of the stone shelf. Saw or felt, she knew they were there, and she also, even in her tears, knew that they were wearing white; perhaps linen garments similar to those worn by our priests. She heard them ask her why she was weeping.

'He's gone!' she told them, in much the words she had used to Peter and me. 'They've taken him! He's not here, and who knows where they've put him!'

As she spoke, she turned her back on the tomb and the white messengers, dismissing them from her mind. She was in no mood for strangers, however unusual, unless they could help her find the body. Not that this was so important of itself, it just seemed to be the only thing, out of all the wreckage of the weekend, that she could focus on.

Even as she turned her back on them, she was accosted by

151

yet another stranger. She felt beset on all sides. This one was standing between the tomb, with Mary beside it, and the ugly upright stakes on the Hill of the Skull, over which the sun had recently risen. Mary assumed it must be the keeper of the garden. There was no good reason for this, other than that the area was clearly well looked after, but Mary was clutching at anything. She would ask and ask, and go on asking anyone who might possibly lead her to Jesus.

This new stranger spoke to her, with the sun behind him, and asked the same question.

'Why are you crying so hard? Who are you searching for that matters so much?'

'Sir,' Mary pleaded, 'if you have taken him, tell me where. I will come and fetch him.'

'Dear Mary!' said Jesus, for it was indeed Jesus, as a less distraught Mary would have realised from the way he asked his question.

'Dear Master!' she replied, standing stock still for an instant and now looking into the sunlight and at Jesus, alive beyond all hope and all expectation. Then she flung herself into his arms. She was still weeping, but it had turned into sobs of surprise mingled with the joy of recognition.

Jesus clasped her to him, and then gently and tenderly eased her away, placing his hands on both her shoulders, so that she could stand upright.

'Don't!' said Jesus. 'The time for clinging is over. I am not yet back in the heart of God who sent me, when we shall share a new intimacy together.' Then he smiled a smile of pure joy and mirth, as if life, all life, but especially his new life, was the most wonderful joke.

'I have a job for you, Mary, my dear,' he said. 'Go and tell our beloved ones, our true family, that I am indeed returning to our Lover, our God. I send you, the first of all of them.'

Looking back, Mary cannot remember how she left Jesus, or he left her. Perhaps there was no parting in any real sense. The next thing that she knew was that she was on her way first to us, and then to Bethany, to tell the story.

I certainly remember the look on her face as she said to me, 'I've seen him,' and told us his message.

It was a strange message, and at first it seemed to imply that he had, dead or alive, now finally left us. I was just beginning to realise that something very important was happening, and that somehow we were at the heart of eternity, but I still could make little practical sense of it.

I was glad for Mary, and I believed her story (although not all did), but it seemed to me to be private to her, and not of immediate relevance to any of the rest of us. In short, I was confused.

I was not alone in this, as I discovered during that day, as our sorry band began to gather again. Groups came back from Bethany, in twos and threes. Joseph and Nicodemus put in an appearance; still wary of their colleagues, but somehow less furtive and more settled, now that they had declared themselves in the burial of Jesus. Peter was devastated by his behaviour in Caiaphas' courtyard (although, of course, he had been braver than most) and by the puzzle of the empty tomb. Andrew was grey and silent, all the sunlight gone out of his life, and he seemed small and fragile. Of Thomas there was no sign; nor had anyone seen him since the arrest of Jesus by the garden. Needless to say, there was no Judas Iscariot, and nor was he mentioned, although his namesake was back among us.

Confusion was the word for all of us. Mary of Magdala persisted in her story, although it was clear that some thought she was hysterical and had imagined the whole thing. Others felt that there might be truth in her story but that it only meant that Jesus had indeed gone back to God, and that it was all over as far as we who were left were concerned. The other Mary felt, weeping, that the whole was a cruel trick of God's, although she didn't say so in so many words.

153

I myself could not believe that Mary of Magdala was deceived. I felt again the aura of the life of eternity that had pervaded the tomb, and the sense that God was working. It was something I had also felt as Jesus so confidently yielded up his life amidst the pain and horror of his suffering on that hideous cross. I began hesitantly to try and say this, but could not find the words. Martha wanted me to say more, and I could see that she was ready to hear, and indeed had the raising of her brother in her thoughts, but nothing I tried made sense. Where I did agree with the majority was that Mary's vision was the last that any of us would see of Jesus, and his words to her were his farewell to all of us. He had left us.

I was soon to find out how wrong I was. That very evening, in fact.

We were upstairs again, with the doors locked. Rumours were flying around Jerusalem, and we had no idea what Caiaphas would do next, but we could well imagine that we would be next in line for his attentions. Fortunately the Passover continues for eight days, and the feast afforded us some protection. Neither Joseph or Nicodemus had any idea what was being discussed, as they were now deeply distrusted by the inner circle of priests and by the party of reform. In any case, the Council did not meet during the festival.

We were sitting more or less silent, apart from the odd desultory comment, when all at once the whole atmosphere changed. We were aware of it immediately, as we were equally instantly aware of Jesus standing smiling in the middle of the room. He didn't suddenly appear, nor was there any sense of magic about it, it just happened that he *was*, there in the midst of us. He face was full of mirth, with the laughter bright in his eyes, shining and spilling out over all of us. Jesus was *present*; in both senses of the word; a gift and here among us, and very much living in the 'now' of life.

He stretched out his hands to us and made a sweeping gesture that embraced us all.

'Peace!' he said. 'My peace be with you all!'

He paused, looking at our faces, and added in the words he had used with us at that last supper, 'Don't look so forlorn! There is no reason to be so fearful. See!'

And with that 'See!' he raised his arms so that his sleeves fell back and we could see the nail-marks in his wrists. This was followed by an economical wriggle of his shoulders (a typical Jesus gesture) and his wide-necked garment slipped down so that we could see the spear-wound under his heart. All the time he was smiling at us with the joy of his new life.

'Peace!' he said again. 'My peace be with you all!' He hitched his garments back into place.

'Just as God, our Lover God, sent me, so I send you,' he continued.

Then, in a way curiously reminiscent of when he washed our feet, he went round us all, breathing on us.

'Breath of Life,' he said. 'I promised you a "Friend", the Spirit. Take it into yourselves.

'You are sent now, and you will offer the life of eternity. All whom you meet must choose, and their choice will become their true selves. You will encounter them for eternity.'

As he breathed on each of us, bending his head in the same gesture with which he had given his life on the cross, he caught and held our eyes. When he came to me, he looked long at me, smiling and twinkling all the time. No words passed, but I heard in my heart his voice, full of strong joy.

'No more partings, Beloved. I am always with you now. I am with our God, our Lover, and with you. The life of eternity begins here.'

As I smiled back at him, full of gladness and infected by his own mirthful joy, I wordlessly offered again my love and service, in every sense an equal of my God who made me his friend. I knew that it was just beginning, and that this would not be easy, and I knew also that Jesus' peace was very different from 'ease' or 'tranquillity'; it would be a very turbulent 'peace'. But I knew that I would now be living life to the full, in all its depths and heights, no longer bound to the time and space in which I happened to exist, and no longer subject to chance and change and death. These things would happen, but they would not be significant within the greater life of eternity which I would now be living with Jesus in his Spirit-Friend.

Thomas (the twin) wasn't there when this happened. He had disappeared from the time of Thursday evening, and we were getting quite worried. Andrew had been out several times looking for him in our usual haunts, but without success.

Thomas turned up on his own account later that week, and would say very little about where he had been. It seemed that by some obscure logic he blamed himself for what had happened on the Thursday and Friday, because of his repeated prognostications that all would end in tears. Indeed, we had each blamed ourselves to some degree.

Thomas had missed out on Sunday's events, but, hearing rumours, eventually made his way to where we were gathered.

True to form, he took the most pessimistic view of what we had to tell him. He thought we were all subject to some mass delusion brought on by a mix of wishful thinking and of misunderstanding of Jesus' words at our final supper. I suspect that Thomas was as much angry as anything else. He felt that we had shared something which he had missed out on. His dismissal of all that we had to say took the form of declaring that unless Jesus appeared to him personally, and allowed him to ram his fingers into the nail-holes and thrust his fist into the wound in Jesus' side, he, Thomas, was having no part in the affair.

The following Sunday, exactly one week after Jesus' first appearance to us, he came again.

Fourth Witness

We were all together in the same place, and this time Thomas was with us, reluctant and still grumbling. Again the feeling of expectancy and brightness suddenly fell upon us all, and Jesus was there. Again, no instant apparition; he simply *was*. Again, with the joy and mirth and fullness of life simply radiating out of him, Jesus gave us his ritual greeting.

'Peace!' he said. 'My peace be with you all!'

Then he turned to Thomas, and a grin spread over his face.

'Well, doubter; oh so angry! Now's your chance.

'See! The wounds in my wrists. Jab as much as you like!' And with his shrug again, there was the wound under his heart.

'See! Big enough even for your fist, Thomas?'

Everything seemed to go slow-motion. Jesus was standing there grinning, almost laughing outright at Thomas. Thomas half raised his hand a couple of times towards Jesus and got no further. His anger was warring with incredulity on his face, both gradually to be replaced by a rueful acceptance, and even the beginnings of a self-deprecatory smile in response to Jesus' whole-hearted amusement.

'Believe it, Thomas!' Jesus said. 'It's much more fun!'

Thomas sank slowly and purposefully to his knees.

'Jesus, my Lord,' he said, gazing up. Then a pause. 'Jesus...God.'

Jesus did laugh out loud now, as he took Thomas by the arms and raised him to his feet to embrace him.

'Right, Thomas, oh so slow. *Now* you understand.'

Then he looked round at all of us, with the message that was to take us out to meet the world and share him abroad.

'You understand because you have seen, and that is good. How good it will be for those who can understand without having to see!'

And that is the whole point. Jesus did many things, some amazing, many unconventional, and he was the most special person to be with that it is possible to imagine. I have only told you a small part of that. But I hope I have told you enough for you to find a flavour of Jesus; enough to realise that to encounter him is to meet God's special envoy, indeed, really to meet God. It could be said that once you have read this far, choice is now upon you, for even not choosing is itself a choice. I have written this so that you, who haven't had our opportunities to see, may still understand, and that this will bring you to the true choices in life, and that you will indeed choose the life of eternity.

Epilogue

The Beloved disciple died last year, and so I, a member of our community, have accepted the task of setting his work in order and giving it to the world. This did not seem so important while he was still with us, telling us his stories and sharing his experience. We were all saddened and disturbed at his death, especially as some had believed he would be with us until the world changed and Jesus be revealed openly at the centre of God's life. The Beloved never took this seriously, and welcomed his death as a part of his life of eternity.

There is a story that he often told that I would like to add to his writings, and this follows, as much in his own words as I can remember, when he would sit under his olive tree, sipping his wine, listening to his inner voice and talking of his friend.

A few weeks after our encounters with the living Jesus in Jerusalem, some of us, mainly the Northerners among us, had made our way back to Galilee. We were staying in Bethsaida, home to most of us in one way or another. Thomas had come to stay, Nathaniel was over from Cana and Mary was up from Magdala.

There was a sense of waiting in the air. We knew we were 'sent' by Jesus in the same way as he had been sent by God, but we felt we should wait for a sign. That is, of course, in the full meaning of the word that Jesus himself had used.

One bright late spring evening, as the sun set enticingly over the hills across the Jordan, Peter suggested a fishing expedition. It was some time since we had taken a boat out, and all of us agreed to this, even Thomas, to whom fishing was entirely new.

It seemed to be a perfect night, and we drifted down the west coast past Capernaum, casting and hauling the net. The night belied its promise, although the exercise and the company made up for the lack of success. Dawn found us close to our old picnic beach, and with an empty boat and empty nets.

As the day brightened, we could make out someone on the shore, standing on the rocks near where one of the springs ran out into the lake. A voice rang out across the water.

'Ahoy there, in the boat. You haven't any fish?'

He sounded as if he expected 'No,' for an answer, and 'No,' was the answer he got.

'There's fish on the starboard side,' he shouted back. 'Cast your nets there.'

We had no idea how he could tell that from the shore, with the light coming from across the lake into his eyes, but we were very willing to try again, if cynical of the outcome.

Over went the net, and as soon as it hit the water it began twitching and jigging in the dance that indicates a catch. And not just any catch; the net was soon silver with fish, and more were leaping and thrashing on the surface of the lake as the net cut its swathe through the school. This was not just a lucky strike, it was astounding.

I looked back at the figure on the shore, and as the light brightened my suspicion hardened into knowledge.

'It's he!' I said to Peter, unnecessarily adding, 'The Lord!'

Peter took one look across, then grabbed a length of rope and tied it round his waist, so that it held his loose fishing smock close to him, and dived overboard. Ordinarily, Peter is a good swimmer, but excitement meant that he more thrashed and splashed his way ashore, rather than swimming any recognisable stroke. He came up onto the shore, and I last saw him kneeling in front of Jesus, before my attention was fully taken with the boat.

The 'desertion' by our captain meant that I was the next most qualified skipper, and we had a job on our hands. There was no way we could get that net aboard without capsizing the boat in the process; it was far too heavy and unwieldy. I settled for towing it to the land, as we were only a hundred yards away, if that.

We ran the prow up onto a small strip of sand, just to the south of the rocks on which Jesus was standing, with Peter still at his feet. We left the boat, and as we walked across to the other two we could see that Jesus had a charcoal fire going, with fish on it, and fresh bread warm on hot stones at the side.

'Bring some of your fish to add to the feast,' smiled Jesus in greeting, and Peter obediently rose and went to the boat. I turned back to help him, and now that the boat was safely grounded we made short work of hauling the net in over the stern and then dragging it forward and onto the land. I should tell you (what fisherman does not count his catch!) that we landed a hundred and fifty three fish that day, all large ones, of many different species, and there was not the tiniest rip or split in the net. How's that for a bumper harvest?

'Come and share breakfast,' Jesus invited, as we returned and added our offering to the fire.

We sat down with him as he broke and shared the bread with us in the old familiar gesture, and did the same with the fish. It was a curious breakfast, passed almost in silence. There was something about this risen Jesus that made small-talk unnecessary. No-one asked him how he was, or where he was staying, or any of the things that one would normally say to a friend who has been elsewhere. The only real question would have been 'Who are you, now?' but in truth we knew the answer to that.

The silence was nevertheless companionable, and I felt my thoughts returning to other meals we had shared with him that began with the breaking of bread when he offered his body to us. I thought of the time he had broken the five loaves and two fishes, and suddenly his arms had been full of the stuff, and I looked across the lake to the knoll, hazy but visible, of that sign.

161

Jesus saw my glance, shared my thought and grinned at me.

'Well done, Beloved,' said his smile. 'Always making the right connections.'

This was our third encounter with the risen Jesus, as a group that is, and each had moved us closer to our new mission. This was to be the one that gave it its final shape. First there had been the catch of fish, and you will by now be familiar enough with Jesus' signs to be able to work it out for yourself. The large and varied catch was a sign of the large number of people from all nations and all walks of life that we were to go and tell about Jesus and his life of eternity. As I thought about the challenge of this, I took comfort from the unbroken net.

But this was not the sum of this morning's encounter, at least not for Peter and myself.

After breakfast, Jesus took Peter for a walk along the beach. As they left, he turned and nodded to me to follow. I did, a few yards behind, but close enough to hear, as Jesus intended.

After a few dozen yards, passed in silence, Jesus stopped and turned to Peter. For the first time since he had risen, Jesus was not smiling. It was as if he had an unpleasant task to perform.

'Simon, son of John, do you love me more than all of this?' he asked, with a wave of his arm at the boat and the sea and the hills of Galilee. The use of Peter's old name, with the patronymic, gave the question a formal, almost legal tone, and I realised that I was there to be a witness.

Peter's response was instant and passionate.

'Yes, of course, you know I love you!'

'Well then,' said Jesus. 'Shepherd my lambs.'

There was a pause, and the formal question came again.

'Simon, son of John, do you love me?'

'Yes, *yes*, you know I love you!'

'That is good,' said Jesus. 'Shepherd my yearlings.'

We walked a little further, and the formality of the

questioning made the next pause with its threefold nature inevitable. I suddenly remembered Peter's triple denial in the courtyard of Caiaphas, and was sure that this was in Peter's mind, too.

'Simon, son of John, *do* you love me?'

'Oh Jesus, you know me inside out, you *know* I love you!' Peter jerked out, close to tears. This questioning hurt him deeply, although I could see that it was also healing.

'That is very good,' said Jesus. 'Be shepherd to my sheep.'

I suddenly realised that Jesus was in fact commissioning the forgiven Peter as a leader in our band. Jesus had talked of himself as the shepherd, and he was now passing the role to Peter, and, given the catch of fish, I'm sure that he had his pagan 'other flocks' in mind.

He had still more to say to Peter.

'Hear then the word of truth. In your youth you tied your own girdle and walked as you pleased. When you are old, others will bind you, your arms outstretched, and you will be carried where you do not please!'

So Peter was, as he had asked during that supper, to walk the same road to death as Jesus. No wonder the sorrow in Jesus' eyes!

A pause, and then Jesus finished with a renewal of Peter's commission, and the smiles were back on both their faces.

'Follow me!' he said, as he put his arm round Peter's shoulders.

Peter had been well aware that I had been asked along as the silent witness of this commissioning, and his next thought was for me, and for my role if he were to be a shepherd. He turned and smiled at me, and then turned back to Jesus with the obvious question on his lips.

'What about our Beloved?' Unspoken, but there in the use of my nickname, was Peter's recognition of the closeness and friendship that Jesus and I shared.

'Our Beloved remains in my heart until all life becomes the

life of eternity. You know that, Peter,' said Jesus. 'Don't worry about the tasks of others. Stick to your own. Dear shepherd, follow me!'

Of the twin tasks Jesus gave to us his people, on the one hand to be sent out, and on the other hand to build the community of love, Peter shepherded the first, and the Beloved made real the second. Some of us had taken Jesus' words to mean that the Beloved would not die, but as you see, Jesus meant something quite different, and rather deeper.

Indeed, it is the Beloved who has been Jesus' witness to all the things you find in this book, and we who have lived with him know the truth of what he has shared with us.

These are only a few of the many stories he told, and I know that they themselves are only a part of all that Jesus said and did. I suppose that if everything were written down, we'd need a library as big as the world.

THIS PART OF THE STORY ENDS HERE

A few words of explanation

I have tried to tell the story of Jesus as told in St John's Gospel, but for 21st-century English readers. Modern scholars have written vast amounts about this short gospel, much of it important and stimulating, and I have taken account of their insights, as many of them as I have encountered, as well as trying to be faithful to the original.

John's Jesus is usually seen against the background of the Jesus of Mark, Matthew and Luke, and this has meant that his strange originality can be concealed. I have tried to tell the story strictly in John's terms, forgetting, as far as one can, the stories of Jesus told by the other three. Hence, for example, the virtual ignoring of an exclusive group called 'the Twelve', an idea that John is aware of, but goes to some lengths to play down.

Like my hero, the hidden writer of the fourth Gospel, I have trusted to imagination and intuition, but also like him, I have not introduced anything that does not seem to be hinted at by the tradition. A case in point would be the restoration of his understanding of disciples to be both women and men, and an honouring of the central part played by women in the fourth Gospel.

I have done my best to be true to the ideas behind the original Greek, so often not immediately translatable into English. Perhaps the clearest example of this sort of problem is the vexed phrase that I have code-named 'the life of eternity'. This is central to Jesus and to anyone's encounter with him, and yet it is untranslatable. The traditional 'everlasting life' is plain misleading, as it has nothing to do with mere extension, and the alternative 'abundant life' is far too weak. I can only hope that the meaning becomes clearer in the context. In any case, it is an idea that takes a lifetime to explore.

Fourth Witness

I said that my hero was the writer of John, but in truth, the hero is Jesus. I want him to escape the quaint straitjacket that has been placed on him by much Christian worship and pious Bible reading, and for us to see him again as his friends and opponents saw him. If this Jesus offends you, then I am sorry for it, but then again, it won't be the first time he has done that.

Kit Widdows
Lindisfarne, October 2000.

Acknowledgements

I can't begin to thank all the dozens of people who helped me in this work. If I just take the example of Richard Knott of Kibbutz HaSolelim and a Bedouin shepherd who between them pointed me to the original Cana in Galilee, they stand for many, many helpers.

John Robinson, sometime Bishop of Woolwich (yes! that Bishop of Woolwich!) opened my eyes to a radically different way of reading John from the accepted churchiness of much interpretation. Don Cupitt, who taught me at college, continues to teach the 'life of eternity' in the present here and now. I owe much to both of them.

I do want to thank Bishop Martin Wharton, the Diocese of Newcastle and especially St Thomas the Martyr Church for supporting me in taking a sabbatical, which allowed me to research the Gospel of John in a way that I could not have done as a busy city-centre priest and Area Dean. I am also very grateful to Professor Chris Rowlands in Oxford for his patience, help and support, along with other members of the New-Testament teaching staff at that university, where I spent the first two months of my sabbatical.

Special thanks go to John and Pauline Pearson, who have freely lent me their cottage on the Holy Island of Lindisfarne on several occasions so that I could 'disappear' in order to write.

And my deepest thanks go to my family. First to the next generation, my children, who have believed in me critically and lovingly throughout this time. They are Heather and Dominic, and also Dominic's wife Maryl, who as a Jew has a special take on my work. Second, my father, another John, who first introduced me to the eccentricities of the fourth Gospel, and now allows me to do the same for him. But most to my wife, Gillian, to whom this book is dedicated, for her constant love, companionship and fending off of the busyness of life to give me space. Whether at the top of a tel in Galilee, deep under the streets of Jerusalem, in the winds of Lindisfarne, or in the city life of Newcastle, she has been there, sharing and encouraging.

And a final thank-you to the unknown author (individual or community of genius) now known as John, and to his hero, Jesus, who has given me at least a toe-hold in the life of eternity. Without that, the whole thing would never have begun.

About the author

My publishers say I should tell you a bit about myself. Not easy, because there is the public and the private me.

The public me is the Area Dean of Newcastle Central Deanery (half time) and the Master of St Thomas the Martyr Church (the city-centre church of Newcastle - also half time) and with some responsibility for Mission and Social Resposibility in the Diocese. What this means in real terms is that I spend 90% of my ministry outside the usual church boundaries. I love this work. I have entrée to two universities, the Civic Centre, the commercial area of Newcastle, and a spectrum of communities ranging from the military to the gay. All these contain people who would love to encounter the Jesus I have written about. I work with Moslems, Hindus, Jews and others of many faiths and none, respecting and listening to their insights and encounters. I am also one of those who acts as a focus for the radical searching Christians in the North-East; I didn't ask for, or expect, this task; but I am delighted that they have chosen to give me it.

The private me is harder, and I will only tell you a bit of the truth. I have loved the fourth Gospel ever since my father read to my sister and myself as children. He would sit on the landing between our bedrooms and read us *Winnie the Pooh, Wind in the Willows, Treasure Island* and *Alice's Adventures in Wonderland*, interlaced with David's exceedingly dubious goings-on in the books of *Samuel*, Moses' adventures in *Exodus* and, from his favourite gospel, John's accounts of his best friend, Jesus.

Ever since, John has never let go of me.

I am, at heart, a scientist, and read Natural Sciences at Cambridge. *Fourth Witness* makes clear that I still start from a scientific view of the world. Theology followed on, both at Cambridge and at Oxford, and I encountered some rubbish and not a little deep pellucid sense about the world we live in.

I discovered; no! rather I am discovering, that at the heart of what is often a sad and backward-looking church, there is a gem of waywardness that echoes and re-incarnates the wayward Jesus of Nazareth. He lives outside the church as much as in, but speaks immediately to me and to the folk to whom I minister.

I am in love with him, and have tried to share that with you, my reader.

This is as much as I will tell you about myself, unless you take me to a pub and share yourself on equal terms with me.

Kit Widdows

Palestine in 30AD

Jerusalem in 30AD

*The Zebedee family house
would be in the Upper City*

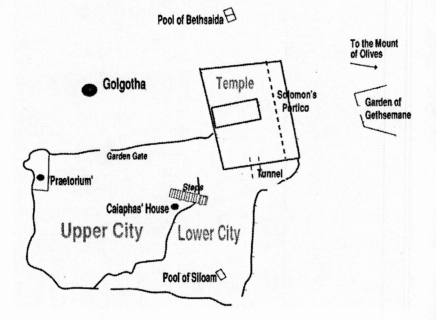

Pool of Bethsaida

To the Mount
of Olives

Golgotha

Temple

Solomon's
Portico

Garden of
Gethsemane

Garden Gate

'Praetorium'

Tunnel

Steps

Caiaphas' House

Upper City

Lower City

Pool of Siloam

Seating in the Upper Room

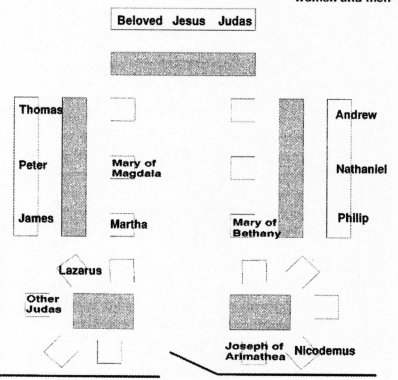

Unnamed seats have other disciples, both women and men

Beloved Jesus Judas

Thomas

Peter

James

Mary of Magdala

Martha

Mary of Bethany

Andrew

Nathaniel

Philip

Lazarus

Other Judas

Joseph of Arimathea Nicodemus

Chapter Sources

Chapter	Story	Fourth Gospel
Prologue	Prologue	1;1-18
1	Foot-washing (UR)	13;1-20
2	First disciples	1;19-end
3	Judas & Peter (UR)	13;21-end
4	Feeding	6
5	Mansions and works (UR)	14;1-11
6	Context & Lazarus	10, 11
7	Context & the Vine (UR)	12;1-19, 15;1-12
8	Cana & Temple cleansing	2
9	You will suffer (UR)	14;27-end, 15;18-16;4
10	Trials of Jesus	5, 7, 8, 9
11	The Paraclete (UR)	14;16-26, 15; 13-17,26f, 16; 5-22
12	Nicodemus, JB and Samaria	3, 4;1-45
13	'Love' (UR)	13;34f, 15;10-17, 14;12-15, 16; 23-end
14	Gentiles	4;46-end, 12; 20-end
15	The Great Prayer (UR)	17
16	Gethsemane to Caiaphas	18;1-27
17	Before Pilate	18;28 - 19;16
18	Crucifixion/Glorification	19;17-end
19	Resurrection	20
Epilogue	Appendix (told by another)	21
	(UR) = In the Upper Room	13-17

Gospel Sources

Reference in *Fourth Gospel*	*Chapter in* *Fourth Witness*
1;1-18	Prologue
1;19-end	2
2	8
3, 4:1-45	12
4;46-end	14
5	10
6	4
7, 8, 9	10
10, 11	6
12;1-19	7
12; 20-end	14
13;1-20	1
13;21-end	3
14;1-11	5
14;12-15	13
14;16-26	11
14;27-end	9
15;1-12	7
15;13-17	11, 13
15;18 - 16;4	9
16;5-22	11
16;23-end	13
17	15
18;1-27	16
18;28 - 19;16	17
19;17-end	18
20	19
21	Epilogue

Printed in the United Kingdom
by Lightning Source UK Ltd.
101009UKS00001B/64-84